P9-DGI-650
COMPLETE
EnglishSmart®
GRADE
6

Grade

Contents 6

Dear Parent,

Thank you for choosing our *Complete EnglishSmart* as your child's learning companion.

We are confident that *Complete EnglishSmart* is the ultimate supplementary workbook your child needs to build his or her English language skills.

Complete EnglishSmart explores the fundamental aspects of language development – listening comprehension, grammar, vocabulary, reading, and writing – by introducing each concept with an easy-to-understand definition and clear examples. This is followed by a variety of interesting activities to provide plenty of practice for your child. There is also a note box at the end of each unit for your child to note down what he or she has learned.

To further ensure that your child retains the language concepts and enjoys the material, there is a review at the end of each section and a Language Games section at the end of the book to help your child consolidate the language concepts in a fun and meaningful way. The accompanying online audio clips (www.popularbook.ca/downloadcentre) let your child practise and develop his or her listening skills.

If your child would like to show his or her understanding of the language concepts in a creative way, we are happy to invite your child on a bonus Language Game Design Challenge. Please find the detailed information on page 271 of this book.

We hope that your child will have fun learning and developing his or her English language skills with our *Complete EnglishSmart*.

Your Partner in Education,
Popular Book Company (Canada) Limited

Don't forget to participate in our ***Language Game Design Challenge*** *on* *p. 271* *for your chance to win a prize!*

Section 1

Listening Comprehension

Scan this QR Code or go to Download Centre at **www.popularbook.ca** for audio clips.

UNIT 1

The Monarch Butterfly

This passage explains general facts about the Monarch butterfly. You will learn how long butterflies have been around for, to which order of insects Monarch butterflies belong, where they are commonly found, how, when, and where they migrate, and their incredible metamorphosis.

Read the questions in this unit before listening. Take notes as you listen. You may read the listening script on page 225 if needed.

Keywords

species
milkweed
Lepidoptera
metamorphosis
migration
phenomena
caterpillar
pupa
transformation
capsule
emerge
temperate
fragile
mysterious

Notes

A. Read the questions. Then check the correct answers.

1. For how long have butterflies been around?

(A) nearly 5 million years

(B) nearly 15 million years

(C) nearly 50 million years

(D) nearly 50 billion years

2. Which order of insects does the Monarch butterfly belong to?

(A) Milkweed

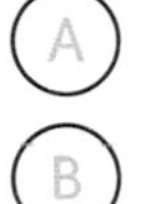

(B) Lepidoptera

(C) the fourth order of insects

(D) Monarchy

3. Which word from the passage means "transformation"?

(A) migration (B) metamorphosis

(C) phenomena (D) capsule

4. How do Monarch butterflies know when it is time to migrate?

(A) when the days get longer

(B) they just know

(C) when the temperature is too warm

(D) when the days get shorter and the air gets cooler

B. Listen to the questions and answer options. Then write the correct letters in the boxes.

C. Write "T" for the true statements and "F" for the false ones.

1. There are nearly 19 000 known species of butterflies. ________
2. Lepidoptera is the fourth largest order of insects. ________
3. Monarchs are recognized by their black wings and red spots. ________
4. The longest route a Monarch can travel is 300 km. ________
5. Monarchs like to fly at night when it is cooler. ________
6. Monarchs can travel up to 130 km a day during migration. ________
7. A favourite destination for Monarchs in winter is central Mexico. ________

D. Answer the questions.

1. What is the great mystery surrounding the Monarch butterfly?

____

____

2. Explain the metamorphosis that the Monarch butterfly goes through.

____

____

____

3. In your opinion, what is the most impressive thing about the Monarch butterfly?

____

____

E. **Listen to the passage "The Monarch Butterfly" again. Then write a summary in no more than 80 words.**

1.1

Include only the main points in the summary. Use your own words.

Summary

Words that I Have Learned

UNIT 2

Leonardo da Vinci - Artist and Visionary

This passage explores Leonardo da Vinci's artistic and scientific achievements. You will learn about some of his most famous paintings, as well as his innovative inventions. You will also learn how Leonardo da Vinci was simply beyond his time.

Read the questions in this unit before listening. Take notes as you listen. You may read the listening script on page 226 if needed.

Keywords	Notes
renowned	
sketch	
invention	
Venice	
chariot	
armoured car	
Milan	
plague	
sewage system	
helicopter	
propel	
pedal	
diving suit	
attachment	

A. Complete the statements by checking the correct answers.

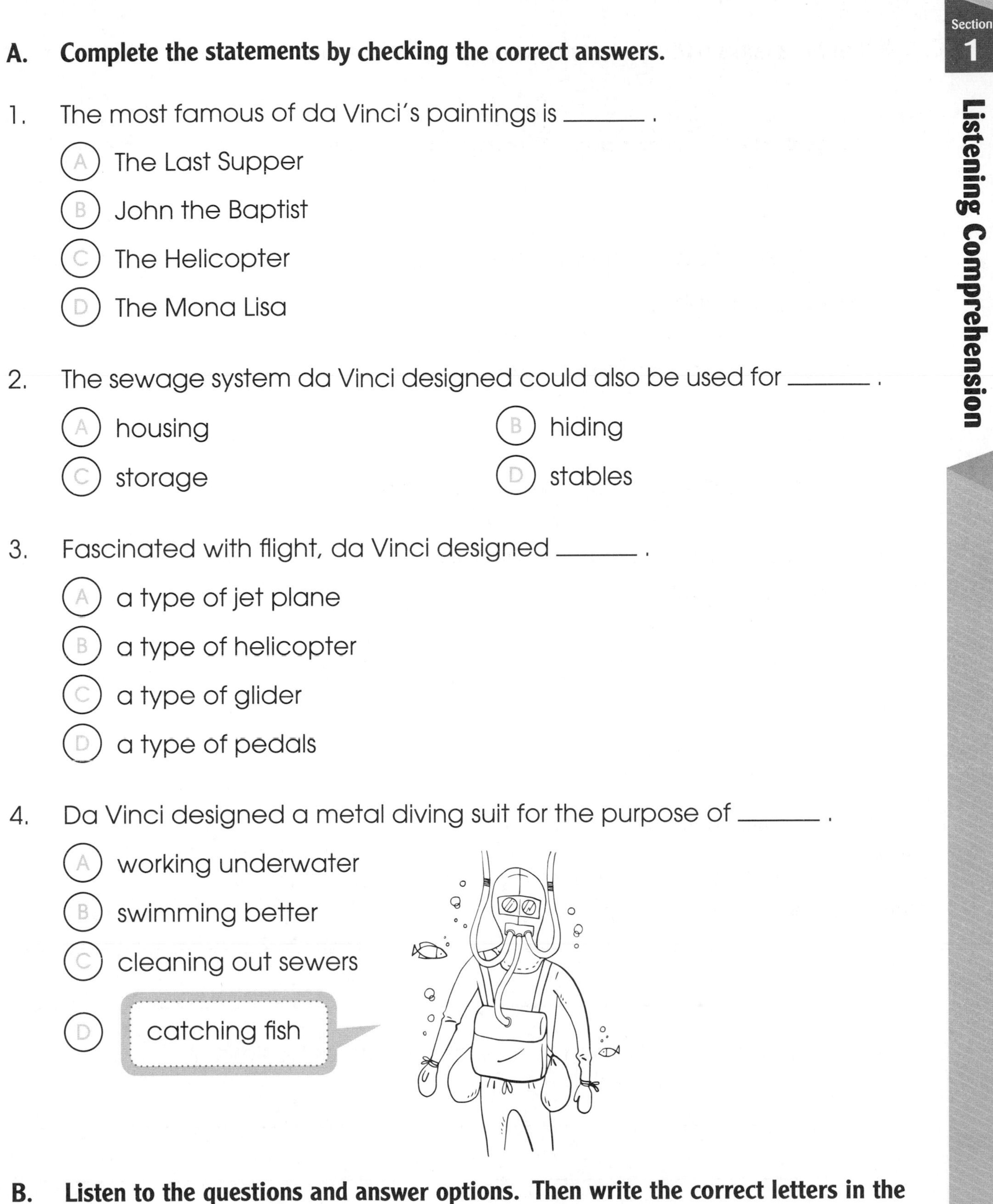

1. The most famous of da Vinci's paintings is ______ .

(A) The Last Supper
(B) John the Baptist
(C) The Helicopter
(D) The Mona Lisa

2. The sewage system da Vinci designed could also be used for ______ .

(A) housing
(B) hiding
(C) storage
(D) stables

3. Fascinated with flight, da Vinci designed ______ .

(A) a type of jet plane
(B) a type of helicopter
(C) a type of glider
(D) a type of pedals

4. Da Vinci designed a metal diving suit for the purpose of ______ .

(A) working underwater
(B) swimming better
(C) cleaning out sewers
(D) catching fish

B. Listen to the questions and answer options. Then write the correct letters in the boxes.

2.2

1 ___ 2 ___ 3 ___ 4 ___

C. Fill in the blanks with the correct words to complete the sentences.

Sforza Castle	propulsion	waistband	drainage	armoured car

1. Da Vinci sketched a drawing of an ________________ with wheels and a crank mechanism.
2. Da Vinci designed a sewage system complete with ________________ for Milan.
3. Da Vinci installed a similar sewage system in ________________ .
4. To aid ________________ underwater, da Vinci designed web-like attachments for the feet.
5. He also designed a ________________ filled with air to keep a person afloat in water.

D. Answer the questions.

1. Explain da Vinci's design of a flying machine.

____

____

2. Why do people say that da Vinci was "ahead of his time"?

____

____

3. In your opinion, what is more impressive: da Vinci's paintings or his sketches of future inventions? Explain.

____

____

E. **Listen to the passage "Leonardo da Vinci – Artist and Visionary" again. Then write a summary in no more than 80 words.**

Include only the main points in the summary. Use your own words.

Summary

Words that I Have Learned

UNIT 3

English – the Language of the World

This passage explains the history and global reach of the English language. You will learn how the English language came to be and how extensive its vocabulary is compared to other languages. You will also learn the significance of the English language today.

Read the questions in this unit before listening. Take notes as you listen. You may read the listening script on page 227 if needed.

Keywords

mother tongue

Mandarin

distribution

dominance

globally

business

expansion

extensive

technical

scientific

telecommunication

correspondence

announcement

agency

Notes

A. Read the questions. Then check the correct answers.

1. Approximately how many people speak English today?

   (A) over one billion
   (B) over two billion
   (C) over three billion
   (D) over four billion

2. Which language is more widely used individually than English?

   (A) Cantonese
   (B) French
   (C) Mandarin
   (D) German

3. How many words does the German language have?

   (A) approximately 100 000
   (B) approximately 185 000
   (C) approximately 6 000 000
   (D) approximately 6800

4. How many people worldwide are potential English speakers?

   (A) half a billion
   (B) one billion
   (C) half a million
   (D) six billion

B. Listen to the questions and answer options. Then write the correct letters in the boxes.

C. Circle "T" for the true statements and "F" for the false ones.

1. About 1/7 of the world's population speaks English today. T / F
2. Julius Caesar brought the English language to England two thousand years ago. T / F
3. There are over 6800 languages in existence today. T / F
4. Roughly half a million widely used technical and scientific terms are not included in the dictionary. T / F
5. Today, over 80% of the world's telecommunications, faxes, and Internet correspondence are written in English. T / F
6. Many educational agencies arrange for English language classes in Germany. T / F

D. Answer the questions.

1. How was the English language spread over the world?

____

____

2. Why is there suddenly a surge in the need to speak English all over the world?

____

____

____

3. What is the advantage of having most of the world speak English?

____

____

____

E. **Listen to the passage "English – the Language of the World" again. Then write a summary in no more than 80 words.**

Include only the main points in the summary. Use your own words.

Summary

____

____

____

____

____

____

____

____

____

____

Words that I Have Learned

____

____

____

____

UNIT 4

The Great Pyramid of Ancient Egypt

This passage talks about the history of the Great Pyramid of Giza and the extravagant pharaoh who built it. You will learn about Khufu, the luxurious life he lived, why he wanted to build the pyramid, and how much work it took to build his monument.

Read the questions in this unit before listening. Take notes as you listen. You may read the listening script on page 228 if needed.

Keywords

mystery
reign
pharaoh
Khufu
throne
luxuriously
afterlife
existence
Giza Plateau
foundation
monumental
mummified
sarcophagus
ceremony

Notes

A. Read the questions. Then check the correct answers.

1. Who built the Great Pyramid?

- (A) Khufu
- (B) Horus
- (C) Ra
- (D) priests

2. What kind of life did Khufu live?

- (A) terrible
- (B) poor
- (C) luxurious
- (D) tiring

3. Where did Khufu want the Great Pyramid to be built?

- (A) on the Land of the Dead
- (B) on the Giza Plateau
- (C) outside Egypt
- (D) on a farm

4. Where did the labourers for the construction of the Great Pyramid come from?

- (A) the Western Desert
- (B) nearby farms
- (C) the Land of the Dead
- (D) the Giza Plateau

B. Listen to the questions and answer options. Then write the correct letters in the boxes.

C. Fill in the blanks with the correct words to complete the sentences.

sarcophagus	labourers	landscape	afterlife
mummified	foundation		

1. Khufu needed thousands of ________________ to build the pyramid.
2. Khufu was ________________ to preserve his body.
3. When Khufu died, he was lowered into a ________________ .
4. The Giza Plateau rose high above the ________________ .
5. Even though Khufu was still young, he knew he had to prepare for the ________________ .
6. Khufu chose the Giza Plateau for his pyramid because the ________________ of the land would support the structure.

D. Answer the questions.

1. Why did Khufu want to build the Great Pyramid?

   ____

   ____

2. How did Khufu treat important guests?

   ____

   ____

   ____

3. What did the priests do after Khufu died?

   ____

   ____

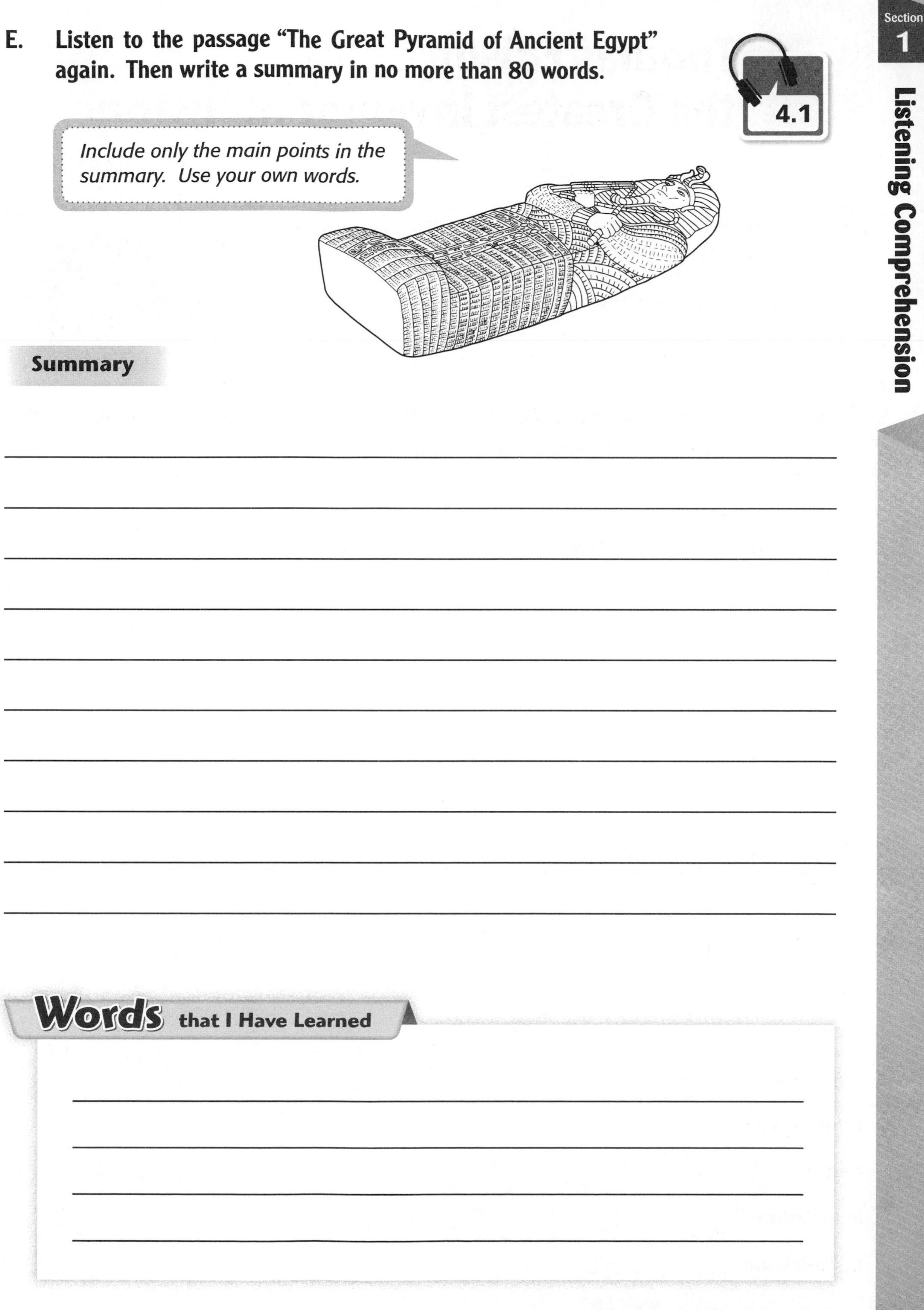

E. **Listen to the passage "The Great Pyramid of Ancient Egypt" again. Then write a summary in no more than 80 words.**

Include only the main points in the summary. Use your own words.

Summary

Words that I Have Learned

UNIT 5

Thomas Edison – the Greatest Inventor in History

This passage explores the life of Thomas Edison. You will learn about Thomas Edison's early life and how he started inventing in the laboratory in the basement of his home. You will also learn about some of his most popular inventions.

5.1

Read the questions in this unit before listening. Take notes as you listen. You may read the listening script on page 229 if needed.

Keywords

patented
discovery
technology
carpentry
laboratory
experiment
freight car
telegraph
device
transmit
microphone
phonograph
genius
inspiration
perspiration

Notes

A. Read the questions. Then check the correct answers.

1. How many patents does Edison hold under his name?

   (A) 18 (B) over 1000
   (C) 1931 (D) 1869

2. Where did Edison's family move when he was seven?

   (A) to New England
   (B) to Ohio
   (C) to New Jersey
   (D) to Michigan

3. What was Edison's job at 12 years old?

   (A) train boy (B) telegrapher
   (C) inventor (D) freight car cleaner

4. Where did Edison set up his first laboratory?

   (A) in the basement of his home
   (B) in an empty classroom
   (C) in an abandoned freight car

B. Listen to the questions and answer options. Then write the correct letters in the boxes.

C. Circle "T" for the true statements and "F" for the false ones.

1. Edison's father was once a scientist. T / F
2. Edison went to school in Port Huron. T / F
3. Edison's mother told him to stop experimenting in their basement. T / F
4. Edison was a roving telegrapher in Canada. T / F
5. The electric light bulb was Edison's only invention. T / F
6. Edison lived till the age of 84. T / F
7. Edison died in a hotel in New Jersey. T / F

D. Answer the questions.

1. Why did Edison's family move to Michigan in the United States?

____

____

2. How can you tell that Edison had a passion for learning even though he skipped classes?

____

____

____

3. What did Edison mean by "Genius is one percent inspiration and ninety-nine percent perspiration"?

____

____

____

E. **Listen to the passage "Thomas Edison – the Greatest Inventor in History" again. Then write a summary in no more than 80 words.**

Include only the main points in the summary. Use your own words.

Summary

____

____

____

____

____

____

____

____

____

____

Words that I Have Learned

____

____

____

____

The Mysterious Bermuda Triangle

This passage explores the mysteries of the Bermuda Triangle. You will learn about where the Triangle is located and some of its characteristics. You will also learn about the disappearance of Flight 19 and some of the natural and supernatural theories about this disappearance.

Read the questions in this review before listening. Take notes as you listen. You may read the listening script on page 230 if needed.

Notes

A. Circle the answers.

1. Which three places does the Bermuda Triangle connect?

   Bermuda, Florida, Puerto Rico

   Bermuda, Georgia, Puerto Rico

   Bermuda, South Carolina, Cuba

2. How many square kilometres of ocean does the Bermuda Triangle cover?

   over 2 million

   over 1.5 million

   over 1 million

3. What was the flight number of the US Navy flight squadron that disappeared?

   Flight 17

   Flight 18

   Flight 19

4. There are ______ main schools of thought on the Bermuda Triangle disappearances.

   one

   two

   three

5. The area the Bermuda Triangle covers is subject to many ______ .

   sudden storms

   intense flurries

   lightning strikes

6. Which ocean current flows through the Bermuda Triangle?

   the South Equatorial Current

   the Gulf Stream

   the North Pacific Current

7. The ocean floor in the Bermuda Triangle is a mixture of ______ .

   coal and algae

   shoals and metals

   shoals and deep trenches

8. Apart from environmental factors, ______ could be the cause of disappearances.

   human error

   mythical sea creatures

   divine intervention

9. How many crew members did the Martin Mariner flying boat have?

   11

   12

   13

10. When did Flight 19 disappear?

    in December 1935

    in December 1945

    in December 1955

B. Listen to the questions and answer options. Then write the correct letters in the boxes.

C. Label the map with the correct information and draw to complete the Bermuda Triangle.

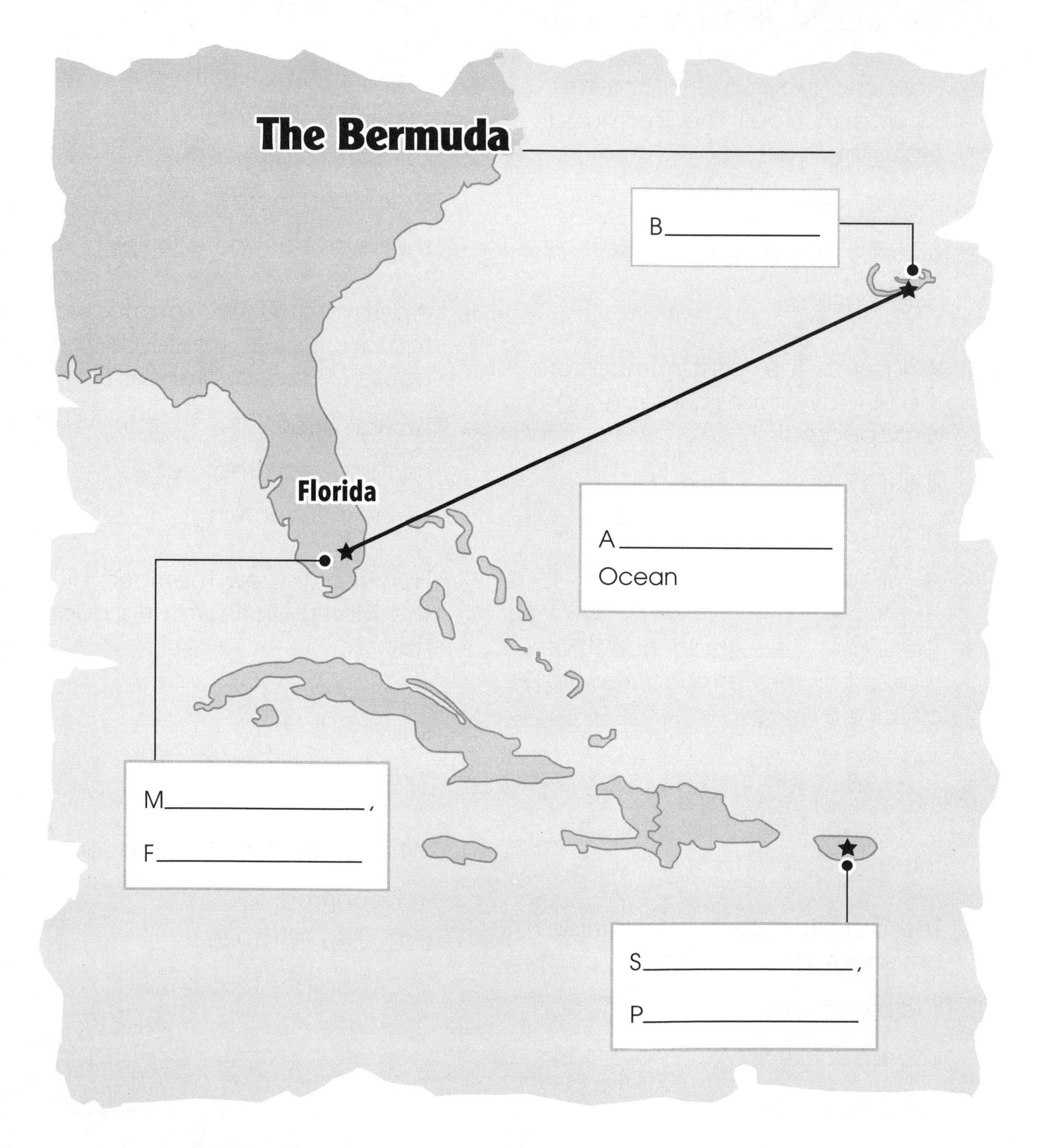

D. Read the statements. Write "R" if they are from a rational school of thought. Write "S" if they are supernatural explanations for the Bermuda Triangle disappearances.

1. Some theorize that the disappearances were the devil's handiwork. ______

2. Some theorize the disappearances occurred because of sudden storms in the Atlantic. ______

3. Some theorize that human error was responsible for the disappearances. ______

4. Some theorize that aliens from other planets were responsible for the disappearances. ______

5. Some theorize the disappearances were just coincidence. ______

6. Some theorize the disappearances occurred because of unpredictable marine conditions. ______

E. Rewrite the statements so that they are true.

1. The most notable Bermuda Triangle disappearance is the vanishing of the Martin Mariner flying boat.

____

____

2. People travel in this area in craft that are large enough to withstand the conditions.

____

____

3. The disappearances of Flight 19 and the Martin Mariner suggest that only natural forces were at work.

____

____

F. **Fill in the blanks in this case file with the correct information.**

SPECIAL INVESTIGATION REPORT

Case Name: The Disappearance of Flight 19	Case Number:
Date: December ________	99

EVENT: The US N____________ flight squadron, F____________ , vanished mysteriously within the Bermuda Triangle, also known as the "D____________ ____________ ", in December 1945.

DETAILS: The Bermuda Triangle spans over a million square kilometres of the A____________ Ocean. The G____________ S____________ , which flows through this area, can swiftly erase e____________ of disasters at sea, which may account for the lack of information on this case.

Some have theorized that s____________ or e____________ forces were at play. The unpredictable m____________ c____________ are a more logical explanation.

However, it is still unclear what transpired. The disappearance of Flight 19, with its crew of ____________ members, remains unsolved.

G. Answer the questions.

1. Describe the environmental factors that may have led to the Bermuda Triangle disappearances.

____

____

____

2. What does the US Coast Guard think about supernatural or extraterrestrial explanations for the disappearances?

____

____

H. Listen to the passage "The Mysterious Bermuda Triangle" again. Then write a summary in no more than 80 words.

R1.1

Listen carefully to make sure you catch all of the important points of the passage to include them in your summary. Use your own words.

Summary

____

____

____

____

____

____

____

____

____

Section 2

Grammar

UNIT 1

Parts of Speech

There are eight **parts of speech** in English: noun, pronoun, verb, adjective, adverb, preposition, conjunction, and interjection.

Example

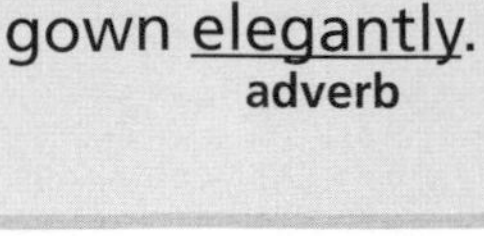

Kathy (noun) wears (verb) her beautiful (adjective) gown elegantly (adverb).

A. Circle the nouns in the sentences.

Noun:
names a person, a place, an object, an idea, or a feeling

1. Beauty is in the eye of the beholder.
2. The teacher wrote a poem about friendship.
3. Where can you find a better place than this?
4. The house was destroyed in the storm.
5. The restaurant serves Italian food.

B. Fill in the blanks with the correct verbs.

Verb:
describes an action or a state of being

surfaced	**hope**	**caused**
reported	**exists**	**revealed**

Numerous people in Scotland have 1. ______________ sightings of the Loch Ness Monster over the years but there has never been scientific evidence that it 2. ______________ . Videos and photographs of the creature have 3. ______________ . However, many have been 4. ______________ as hoaxes. The Loch Ness Monster has not 5. ______________ harm to humans and many people still 6. ______________ to see it.

C. Underline the adjectives in the paragraph.

Adjective:

describes a noun or a pronoun

It is difficult to argue that hockey is not the national passion of Canadians. Canada, with its frigid weather in the winter, is suitable for playing hockey. As early as 1870, British soldiers stationed in Halifax started playing hockey on frozen ponds around the city. In 1892, Lord Stanley, the Governor General of Canada, donated a silver bowl to be awarded to the best amateur team. That was the origin of the Stanley Cup.

D. Rewrite the sentences by adding adverbs.

Adverb:

modifies the meaning of a verb, an adjective, or another adverb

1. Carmen finished all the pasta.

____

2. They went down the steep slope.

____

3. He was not good at swimming so he signed up for a swimming course.

____

____

4. He nodded and started figuring out how to settle the matter.

____

____

E. Circle the correct pronouns to complete the paragraph.

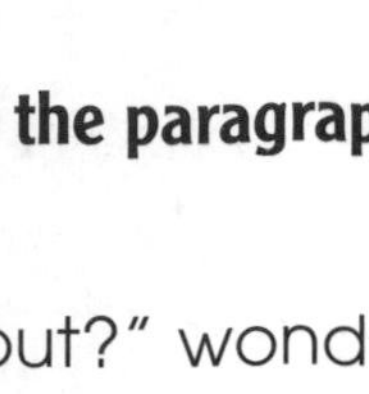

Pronoun:

stands in for a noun

" **What / I** on earth is the gossip about?" wondered Ted. At first, **he / they** thought that **he / it** was the one his neighbours were talking about but soon realized that **they / it** were not talking about **him / it** . **She / He** was just being too sensitive and had almost made a fool of **itself / himself** . Luckily, Ted's sister did not know about **this / those** or **she / they** would tell their parents. Ted promised **herself / himself** never to eavesdrop on others' conversations again.

F. Circle the correct prepositions. Then cross out the wrong ones and write the correct prepositions above them.

Preposition:

expresses the relationship between words

Joanne Kathleen Rowling, author ~~with~~ of the immensely popular Harry Potter series, went through ordinary existence to stardom virtually overnight. The fame bestowed upon her was beyond her wildest dreams. As a single parent, with little money, Joanne often headed to a café for write about the wizarding world of magic. This imaginative series has now sold over 450 million copies and has been adapted with a blockbuster film franchise. Her success shows that you can achieve anything if you put your mind of it.

G. **Complete the sentences with the correct conjunctions and interjections.**

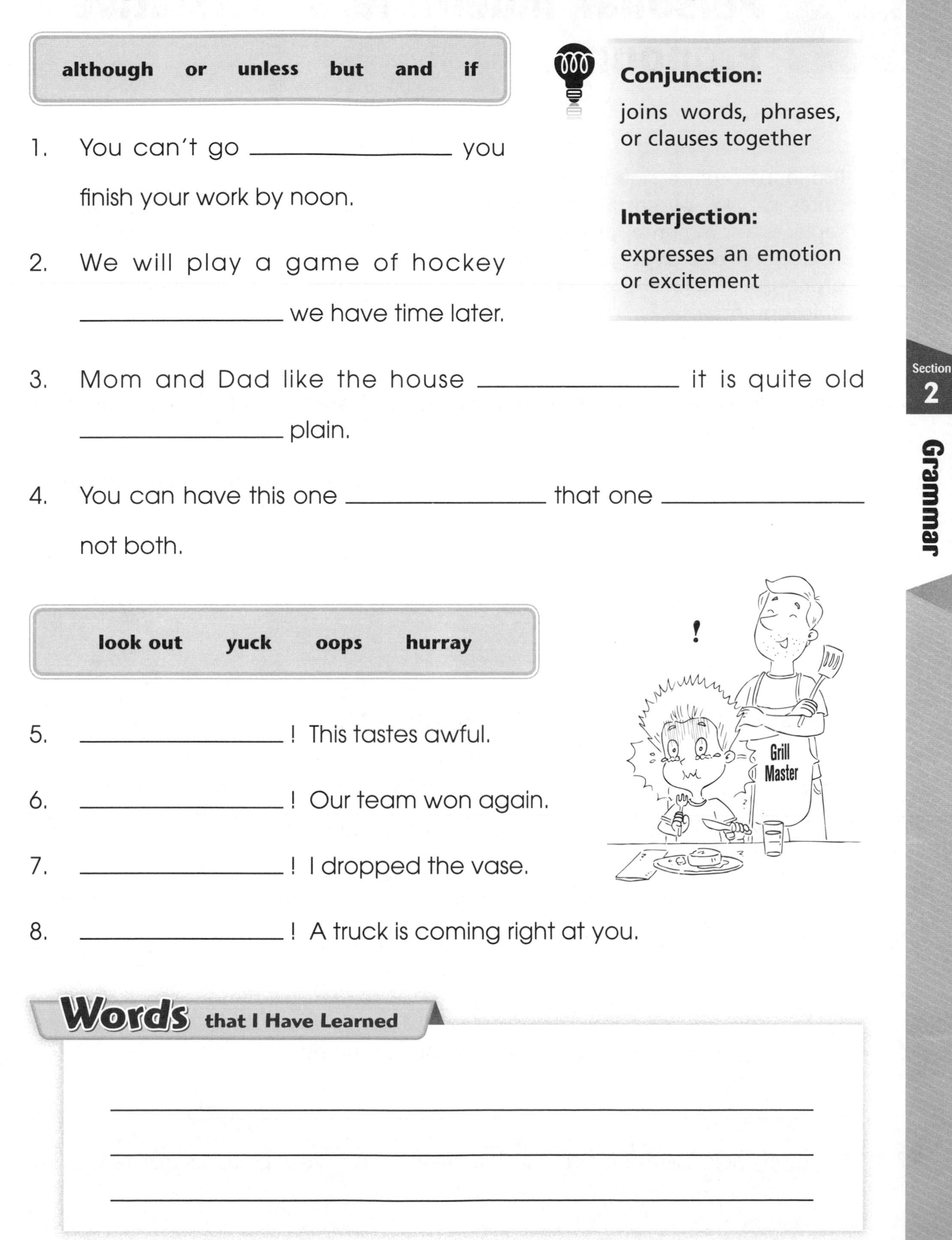

although	or	unless	but	and	if

Conjunction:
joins words, phrases, or clauses together

Interjection:
expresses an emotion or excitement

1. You can't go ______________ you finish your work by noon.
2. We will play a game of hockey ______________ we have time later.
3. Mom and Dad like the house ______________ it is quite old ______________ plain.
4. You can have this one ______________ that one ______________ not both.

look out	yuck	oops	hurray

5. ______________! This tastes awful.
6. ______________! Our team won again.
7. ______________! I dropped the vase.
8. ______________! A truck is coming right at you.

Words that I Have Learned

____

____

____

Section 2 Grammar

UNIT 2

Personal, Indefinite, and Relative Pronouns

Pronouns replace nouns and noun phrases. A **personal pronoun** replaces a common or proper noun. There are two types of personal pronouns: subject pronouns and object pronouns.

Example

Willa lent her pen to the boy.
proper noun — common noun

She lent her pen to him.
personal subject pronoun — personal object pronoun

A. Rewrite the sentences by replacing the underlined words with the correct personal subject pronouns.

A personal subject pronoun replaces the subject of a sentence: I, you, he, she, it, we, they.

1. Ella had a bad dream.

____

2. Jane and I sit beside each other in class.

____

3. Laura and Jay joined the chess club yesterday.

____

4. The baby let out a loud wail as the mother gave birth.

____

5. Jason always helps wash the dishes after dinner.

____

6. You and Brian should watch the new horror movie.

____

7. You and I had better clean up this mess before your parents come home.

____

B. Fill in the blanks with the correct personal object pronouns.

A personal object pronoun replaces the object of a sentence: me, you, him, her, it, us, them.

1. My dad bought a bike for my sister. Today, he will give it to ______________ .

2. Do you know Justin Wallis? Have you seen ______________ ?

3. I often give my old clothes to charities. I give them all to ______________ .

4. Mom gave me a list of groceries. Now I have to buy ______________ .

5. The bus driver just let my friends and me on the bus for free. He did not even look at ______________ .

C. Circle the correct pronouns to complete the sentences.

1. **I / Me** got a new laptop for my birthday!

2. My grandma bought it for **I / me** !

3. Gary could not wait to show **we / us** his new painting.

4. **They / Them** own the new bakery on Unionville Street.

5. I will never tell my secret to **she / her** . **She / Her** cannot keep secrets.

6. The chef thinks that the cheesecake **he / his** makes is the best.

7. Mr. McGregor handed our tests back to **we / us** . **It / He** was not happy with our scores.

Indefinite pronouns are pronouns that do not refer to anyone or anything specific. They can be singular or plural.

Examples

- Someone is baking a cake. (singular)
- Anything can happen. (singular)
- Many of the people voted. (plural)

D. Fill in the blanks with the correct indefinite pronouns.

Indefinite Pronouns	
all	anything
several	everyone
both	each
no one	anybody
none	some

1. Can ______________ give me a hand with these bags, please?
2. I do not need too many potatoes for this. ______________ should be enough.
3. I read ______________ of the book last night. I'll read the rest tomorrow night.
4. ______________ you need to know about the movie is that it will be very funny.

5. ______________ of the kids wanted the vegetables so I ate them instead.
6. Grace and Tammy were extremely tired. ______________ of them wanted to go home and sleep.
7. Is there ______________ I can help you with, sir?
8. ______________ of the twin brothers wanted his own bedroom.
9. ______________ told me where the washroom is so I will find it myself.
10. I am happy that ______________ loves the chocolate cake I baked.

A **relative pronoun** relates a phrase or clause to a noun or pronoun that is mentioned earlier in a sentence.

Example

The boy <u>who</u> gave you the cookie is my brother.

E. Circle the correct relative pronouns to complete the sentences.

1. Arlene wore the dress ______ her mom sewed for her to the party last night.

   that   whose   whom

2. I have four siblings, one of ______ is a boy.

   whom   which   that

3. My best friend, ______ gift I'm holding, is turning ten today!

   which   whose   whom

4. The grade, ______ I get, will be well deserved.

   whoever   whomever   whichever

5. This shirt, to ______ it belongs, had better be clean.

   whoever   whomever   whichever

6. ______ finds the lost dog will receive a reward.

   Whoever   Whomever   Whichever

Words that I Have Learned

____

____

____

UNIT 3

Verb Tenses

Verbs have different tenses. The **simple present tense** is used with facts, current actions, habitual actions, and general truths.

Examples

- Most birds fly. (fact)
- Dad works for that company. (current action)
- I go to bed at nine every night. (habitual action)
- The sun rises in the east. (general truth)

A. Add the correct ending to turn the verb into the correct forms in the simple present tense. If no ending is needed, leave it blank.

Add "s" or "es" to the base form of a verb for a third person singular subject.

1. Antonio leave_______ his clothes everywhere.
2. Toys belong_______ in the toy box.
3. Bessie always correct_______ my grammar.
4. Marissa love_______ her pet birds.
5. Sasha clean_______ her room every night before she go_______ to bed.
6. Sean and Nelson play_______ video games all afternoon every Saturday.
7. Nelli trust_______ Erica and is sure that she trust_______ her too.
8. Dad stress_______ too much about work.
9. I volunteer_______ at the local hospital every weekend.
10. My dog Antoine whine_______ whenever I leave the house.
11. The bunny in the hat vanish_______ in the blink of an eye.

The **simple past tense** expresses past actions.

Add "d" or "ed" to the base form of most verbs to change them to the past tense.

Examples

- I baked a cake yesterday.
- She walked home last night.
- We joined the summer camp last year.

B. Write the verbs in the simple past tense to complete the sentences.

1. Lucy ________________ (finish) getting ready ten minutes ago.
2. Yesterday afternoon, Ada ________________ (continue) studying for her test.
3. Two prisoners ________________ (escape) from jail last night.
4. I did not know that this rare bird ________________ (exist) all this time.
5. The boy ________________ (polish) the gentleman's shoes after his lunch break.
6. Isabella ________________ (post) her first photo online just a few seconds ago.
7. We ________________ (point) to the CN Tower after the tourist asked us for directions.
8. Mom ________________ (plant) some flowers in our backyard early this morning.
9. Last Sunday, my parents and I ________________ (dine) at a Spanish restaurant near our home.
10. Cliff ________________ (cough) on me yesterday so now I'm sick.
11. The doctor ________________ (advise) me to take some medicine.

The **simple future tense** expresses future actions.

Add "will" before the base form of a verb to change it to the simple future tense.

Example

Nora will watch the movie tomorrow night.

C. Fill in the blanks with the correct verbs in the simple future tense.

visit	help	have	name	meet
create	write	last	rain	practise

1. I ____________ you at the entrance before the game starts.
2. The water in Vera's water bottle ____________ her all day long.
3. My parents ____________ my baby sister when she is born.
4. Leonardo ____________ every weekend after his new drums are delivered.
5. The weatherman says it ____________ for the next four days.
6. My brother Benjamin ____________ you with your homework after school.
7. Shirley and Jonathan ____________ a new piece of art for the display together.
8. Michelle ____________ Jack a letter when she returns home from vacation.
9. They ____________ a garage sale this weekend to sell the things they do not need.
10. Grandpa and Grandma ____________ us in a few weeks.

Irregular verbs do not follow the rules of tenses. Their past tense forms may be spelled the same as or very differently from their base forms.

Examples

Base Form	Past Tense Form
spread	spread
catch	caught

D. Write the given verbs in the correct forms in the simple present, simple past, and simple future tenses.

Simple Present

1. Dana ________________ (keep) leaving the door unlocked.
2. Rocky ________________ (bring) an apple for lunch every day.
3. Mom ________________ (drive) me to school every morning.

Simple Past

4. The baby ________________ (sleep) soundly last night.
5. Rosa ________________ (pay) too much for lunch yesterday.
6. Kate ________________ (blow) out the candles when we finished singing the birthday song.

Simple Future

7. I ________________ (leave) the party early tonight.
8. Omar ________________ (begin) band practice tomorrow.
9. This T-shirt ________________ (shrink) if you wash it in hot water.

Words that I Have Learned

____

____

____

UNIT 4

Progressive Tenses

Progressive tenses show continuous actions. The **present progressive tense** shows an ongoing action happening in the present.

Example

Donna is talking on the phone with her best friend now.

A. Check the sentence if it is in the present progressive tense. If not, rewrite it in the present progressive tense.

1. Libby is running to school because she has missed the school bus. ◯
2. The baby is sleeping soundly even though the pet dog keeps barking. ◯
3. Jade visited the zoo with her friends. ◯
4. Haley and Logan are accepting their awards. ◯
5. The soccer team is not arriving by airplane. ◯
6. Is Ms. Walsh teaching today? ◯
7. The chefs make delicious desserts. ◯
8. I did not attend the ceremony. ◯
9. Helen is writing her speech. ◯

Do not forget the negative and interrogative forms!
e.g. She is not talking.
Is she talking?

Rewritten Sentences in the Present Progressive Tense

____

____

____

The **past progressive tense** shows an action that was ongoing at a particular time in the past or over a period of time in the past.

Example

Alia was baking muffins last night.

B. Fill in the blanks with the verbs in the past progressive tense.

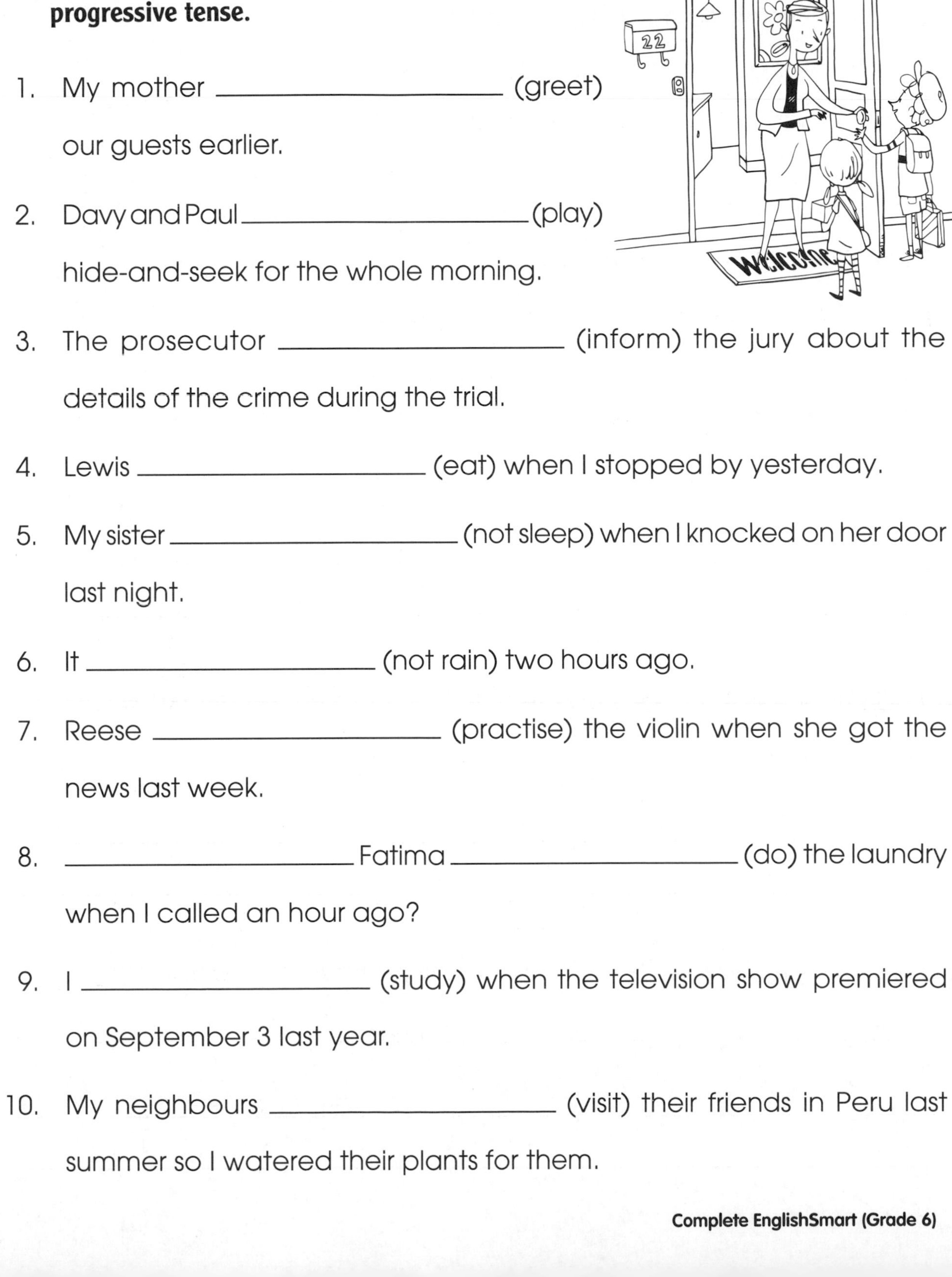

1. My mother ____________________ (greet) our guests earlier.
2. Davy and Paul ____________________ (play) hide-and-seek for the whole morning.
3. The prosecutor ____________________ (inform) the jury about the details of the crime during the trial.
4. Lewis ____________________ (eat) when I stopped by yesterday.
5. My sister ____________________ (not sleep) when I knocked on her door last night.
6. It ____________________ (not rain) two hours ago.
7. Reese ____________________ (practise) the violin when she got the news last week.
8. ____________________ Fatima ____________________ (do) the laundry when I called an hour ago?
9. I ____________________ (study) when the television show premiered on September 3 last year.
10. My neighbours ____________________ (visit) their friends in Peru last summer so I watered their plants for them.

The **future progressive tense** shows an ongoing action that will be happening over a period of time in the future.

Example

The people will be marching in the protest tomorrow.

C. Rewrite the sentences in the future progressive tense with the given words.

1. Carly is memorizing her lines for the play.
2. My dad was building the tree house last week.
3. Jess and Sam were working on the project when I called them.
4. I am canoeing at the Port Perry Marina.
5. She is cooking pasta for dinner.
6. The children are playing basketball the whole summer.

Future Progressive Tense e.g. Mina will be travelling next week.

1. tomorrow morning 2. this weekend

1. ______________________________
2. ______________________________

In Negative Form e.g. Mina will not be travelling next week.

3. tomorrow 4. next Saturday

3. ______________________________
4. ______________________________

In Interrogative Form e.g. Will Mina be travelling next week?

5. this Friday 6. next summer

5. ______________________________
6. ______________________________

D. **Circle the correct progressive tense in each sentence.**

1. **Will Matias be coming / Was Matias coming** to my birthday party tonight?
2. Ellen **is wearing / will be wearing** a thick coat because it is chilly.
3. The clown **is performing / was performing** for the children ten minutes ago.
4. Dany **is not listening / was not listening** to your joke when you said it this morning.
5. **Is Justine painting / Was Justine painting** her room last weekend?
6. Mike **will be washing / was washing** the dishes when his sister took the garbage out.
7. The Martins **was flying / will be flying** to Australia this time tomorrow.
8. Pat **was jogging / will be jogging** in the park when it started snowing.
9. Janice **is waiting / was waiting** for her mom to pick her up now.
10. John **was driving / is driving** to the city last evening.

Words that I Have Learned

____

____

____

Section 2 Grammar

UNIT 5 Verbals

Verbals are formed from verbs but they function as nouns, adjectives, or adverbs.

Gerunds end in "ing" and function as nouns.

Participles are used as adjectives.

Infinitives can be nouns, adjectives, or adverbs. They are the "to" form of verbs.

Examples

- Fishing is Dad's favourite hobby. (gerund: Fishing)
- They found the hidden treasure. (past participle: hidden)
- The washing machine works well. (present participle: washing)
- To win is the most important thing. (infinitive: To win)

A. Underline the verbals in the sentences. Then write the sentence numbers in the correct boxes.

1. We enjoy swimming on a hot summer day.
2. The cooling fan is very noisy.
3. The snow made it hard for us to see.
4. Judy made herself a laughing stock.
5. Some say that cooking is an art.
6. To settle down is what concerns him most.
7. My parents enjoy jogging in the morning.
8. The kids greeted the crossing guard warmly.
9. Grandpa does not like driving at all.
10. They were about to leave when they heard someone knock at the door.
11. Keith admires his uncle, who is a devoted scientist.

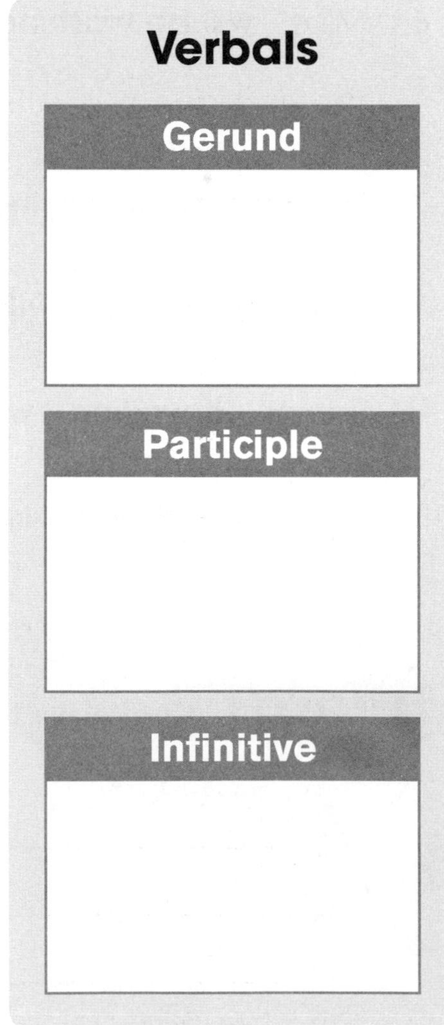

B. Fill in the blanks with the correct gerunds to complete the sentences.

shopping	**volunteering**	**skydiving**	**dancing**
resting	**canoeing**	**smiling**	**dreaming**
hiking	**counting**	**snowboarding**	**leading**

1. ____________ would be such a thrill!
2. ____________ is a brain activity that most people cannot control.
3. Betty's favourite thing to do on Saturday is ____________ because she always finds something on sale.
4. When the girls arrived at the party, there was already so much ____________ and singing.
5. ____________ is the best thing to do in the peaceful mountains.
6. This winter, my friends and I are going to a ski resort to learn ____________ .
7. ____________ is an important skill to learn in kindergarten.
8. Henri went ____________ when he stayed at the cottage by Lake Muskoka.
9. ____________ is an important part of becoming class president.
10. Leroy likes helping others. He always says that ____________ is a good way to spend your weekend.
11. ____________ can make you and everyone around you happy.
12. ____________ is necessary if you are sick and want to feel better soon.

C. Read each sentence. Write "G" if it contains a gerund and "P" if it contains a participle.

1. Painting will always be Luna's first love.
2. Peggy put on her dancing shoes and walked gracefully onto the dance floor.
3. The winning team cheered as they were presented with their trophy.
4. Singing is my true passion.
5. Who knew whistling could be so much fun?
6. My sister Salma is talented at acting.
7. The wandering nomad arrived in town today.
8. There are still some cookies on the baking sheet.

D. Circle the correct verbal for each sentence.

1. Russel likes **stargazed / stargazing** whenever the sky is clear.
2. You need **hiked / hiking** boots to protect your ankles.
3. **Baking / Baked** is a therapeutic activity for me.
4. This is a book that no one wants **read / to read** .
5. Jerry is happy to find his **lost / losing** robot.
6. **Daydreaming / Daydreamed** may help build your creative mind but do not forget to come back to reality.
7. I cannot wait **decorating / to decorate** for Halloween.
8. Living things need food and water **survived / to survive** .

E. Use each verb in a sentence as a gerund, a participle, and an infinitive.

Words that I Have Learned

Section 2

Grammar

UNIT 6 Phrases

A **phrase** is a group of words that has no subject or predicate.

A **verbal phrase** contains a gerund, a participle, or an infinitive. It functions as a noun, an adjective, or an adverb.

Examples

- Fishing in the bitter cold is a test of will.
- Having won the race, the athlete waved at the crowd.
- He does not want to leave her behind.

A. Underline the gerund phrase in each sentence.

1. Eating dinner is my favourite part of the day.
2. Camille thought she could pass the exam by studying all night.
3. Waiting for the bus can make anyone impatient.
4. Meeting new people always makes me nervous.
5. Winning the writing contest meant a lot to Dolores.
6. Painting landscapes is my mom's expertise.
7. Attending red carpet events made the young actress feel overwhelmed.
8. Walking in the heavy rain is not a good experience.
9. Drinking a cup of hot chocolate was the best reward after skiing.
10. Lee is good at making new friends.

B. Underline the participle phrase in each sentence. Then circle the noun it modifies.

1. Screaming wildly, the child threw a tantrum in the store.

2. The ballerinas dancing in the front row are supposed to be the best.

3. Terrified of falling off, Devin hung on tightly to the horse's reins.

4. Exhausted after hours of practice, the boys suggested taking a rest.

5. Knowing it was wrong, Lina still cheated on the test.

6. My muffins baking in the oven will be very delicious.

7. Lost in the mall, Jessica finally asked for directions.

C. Identify whether each infinitive phrase is used as a noun "N", an adjective "ADJ", or an adverb "ADV".

1. To complete the work in one day is impossible.

2. She wanted to learn knitting.

3. The children went home to eat their supper.

4. Her mom made her a dress to wear to the party.

5. The team was not ready to quit the game.

6. Do you have used books to donate to less fortunate children?

7. Rebecca attended university to earn a science degree.

D. **Write sentences using the following gerund, participle, or infinitive phrases.**

Verbal Phrases

- A skating on the frozen pond
- B stuck in a traffic jam
- C tired of waiting
- D to come up with ideas
- E trapped in the elevator
- F writing a journal entry
- G enjoying a lazy afternoon
- H to be a good basketball player
- I camping in the provincial park
- J satisfied with the results
- K to write an e-mail
- L watching the stars

A ______________________________

____

B ______________________________

C ______________________________

D ______________________________

E ______________________________

F ______________________________

G ______________________________

H ______________________________

I ______________________________

J ______________________________

K ______________________________

L ______________________________

E. Complete the sentences with the specified verbal phrases.

GP : gerund phrase

PP : participle phrase

IP : infinitive phrase

1. **PP** ____________________, Dad took us on a ski trip.

2. I really enjoyed **GP** ____________________.

3. My sister looked helpless **PP** ____________________.

4. She discovered a mitten **PP** ____________________.

5. I could see that many beginner skiers preferred **IP** ____________________

   ____________________.

6. **GP** ____________________ was much more difficult than I had thought.

7. **GP** ____________________ was the best I could do.

8. **IP** ____________________, I am going to take skiing lessons.

Words that I Have Learned

____

____

____

UNIT 7

More on Phrases

A **noun phrase** is made up of a noun and all its modifiers.

Examples

- All grade one students were told to stay in the gym.
- They were waiting in a small and stuffy room.

A. Check if the underlined words in the sentences are noun phrases. If not, circle the noun phrases.

1. The red, sleek sports car sped past me.
2. The man sitting on the bench is Mr. Miller.
3. We were all exhausted after the long, uphill climb.
4. She always enjoys a cool, refreshing drink in summertime.
5. We never expected such a warm and welcoming reception.
6. There are altogether seven honour students.
7. Mother baked a delicious cheesecake for us.
8. The long, bumpy ride lasted forever.
9. I thought it was an extremely boring movie.
10. I was shocked to see the fluffy, creepy thing.
11. We did not know what that thick, oily, green substance was.
12. He is the most skilful player we have ever met.

Examples

An **adjective phrase** describes a noun or a pronoun as an adjective does.

An **adverb phrase** describes a verb as an adverb does.

- This <u>steaming hot chicken</u> soup is delicious. (adjective phrase)
- I know <u>quite surely</u> what she wants. (adverb phrase)

B. Write adjective and adverb phrases to complete the sentences.

Adjective Phrase

1. I like my ______________________ puppy.
2. The ______________________ woman is my aunt.
3. The ______________________ backpack belongs to my sister.
4. The ______________________ clowns bumped into one another.
5. The ______________________ man did not allow us in.
6. Who wants to have a ______________________ sandwich?
7. My parents bought me a ______________________ T-shirt.

Adverb Phrase

8. The hurricane blew ______________________ .
9. The grade six boys were practising ______________________ .
10. All of us waited ______________________ .
11. Andrew stopped ______________________ .
12. The sprinters dashed ______________________ .
13. The children walked ______________________ .
14. The choir sang ______________________ .

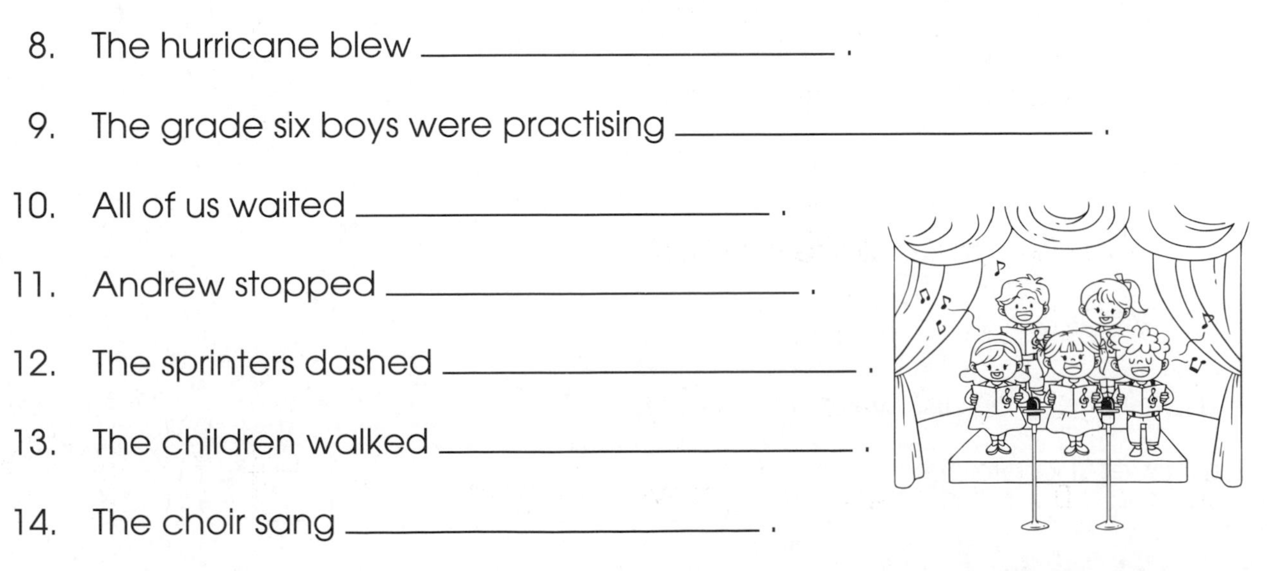

Many adjective phrases and adverb phrases are introduced by prepositions. A preposition is a linking word between a noun or a pronoun and other words in a sentence.

Examples

- The tourists on the boat are amazed by the sight. (on the boat: adjective phrase)
- The soldiers marched across the field. (across the field: adverb phrase)

C. Underline the adjective phrase or adverb phrase in each sentence and circle the preposition. Then write whether it is an adjective phrase (Adj) or an adverb phrase (Adv) in the parentheses.

1. The coach of the opposing team did not think it was fair. ( )
2. That afternoon, all the workers assembled in the compound. ( )
3. The fugitive crawled through the tunnel and escaped. ( )
4. The members of the team were each given a name tag. ( )
5. No one from his group wanted to do the presentation. ( )
6. Fred played video games from morning to night. ( )
7. All the guests waited in the hallway. ( )
8. His little dog managed to jump across the ditch. ( )
9. The food in the cooler had gone bad. ( )
10. He climbed up the tall tree to save the cat. ( )
11. The guards of the palace ordered us to leave. ( )
12. The red jelly beans were scattered all over the place. ( )

D. **Circle the correct phrase as specified to complete each sentence.**

Adjective Phrase

1. We saw a movie ______ last night.

   about superheroes — at the theatre

2. Kelly ate the cake ______ .

   after dinner — with a strawberry on it

3. The caretaker ______ nursed the injured bird back to health.

   very patiently — of our school

Adverb Phrase

4. He read the book ______ .

   from the library — before lunch

5. The children ______ enjoyed the show.

   from the daycare centre — quite surprisingly

6. The puppy ______ wagged its tail when it saw us.

   very happily — of our neighbour

Words that I Have Learned

____

____

____

UNIT 8 Active and Passive Voice

A sentence can be in the active or passive voice.

A sentence is in the **active voice** when the subject performs the action of the verb.

A sentence is in the **passive voice** when the subject receives the action. The performer of the action is mentioned at the end of the sentence.

Examples

- Active Voice:
  Estelle sings a song.
- Passive Voice:
  The song is sung by Estelle.

A. Circle "A" if the sentences are in the active voice; circle "P" if they are in the passive voice.

A or P

1. Mikayla and Jamie danced to the beat together. **A** **P**
2. Jerome sang the national anthem during the ceremony. **A** **P**
3. The winning goal was scored by Fareed. **A** **P**
4. Molly argued her point to her teacher. **A** **P**
5. Dinner is prepared every night by Mom. **A** **P**
6. The wedding gown was tailored by Mr. Fugima. **A** **P**
7. The audience applauded the performers. **A** **P**
8. The speech was given by the top student. **A** **P**
9. Dr. Korsov successfully built a life-sized robot. **A** **P**
10. The participants ran the marathon in the rain. **A** **P**

B. Underline the verb, circle the performer of the action, and put the object receiving the action in parentheses in each sentence.

Examples

Janet writes (a book).

performer — action — receives the action

(A book) is written by Janet.

receives the action — action — performer

1. Mrs. Kelcher was directing a musical production.

2. The musical production was introduced by Principal Santos.

3. The musical would be attended by the entire school.

4. Richard and Ivy created the costumes.

5. The props were made by the art students.

6. Andre wrote the songs for the school musical.

7. The students rehearsed the musical one last time before the performance.

8. Many teachers, students, and their parents attended the show.

9. The actors read their lines backstage.

10. Sharon conducted the band.

11. The music was played by the school band.

12. The audience cheered at the end of the band's performance.

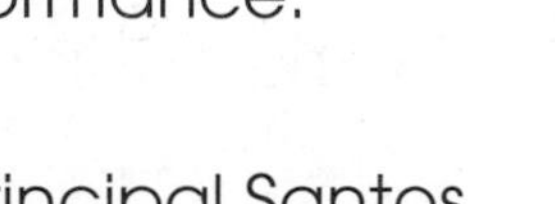

13. Every actor was congratulated by Mrs. Kelcher and Principal Santos.

C. Rewrite the sentences.

Active Voice → Passive Voice

1. Grace Shelby created the Shelby Food for Kids Foundation.

   ____

2. Dr. Godfried discovered a rare dinosaur fossil.

   ____

3. 2.3 million viewers watched the match of the century.

   ____

4. My sister cooked all the dishes for the meal.

   ____

5. Jeremy posted the notice on the board.

   ____

Passive Voice → Active Voice

6. The spam e-mail was received by all of my friends.

   ____

7. The overdue library book was returned at last by Eunice.

   ____

8. The package was delivered by an anonymous person.

   ____

9. The special menu was created by Chef Aguilar.

   ____

10. All the cabinets were assembled by Dad.

    ____

Many sentences can be written in both active and passive voice, but sometimes a sentence in the passive voice may sound awkward.

Also, the performer of the action can be omitted in a passive voice sentence if the performer is obvious or unknown.

Examples

- Orange juice is drunk by Nadine. ✗
- A message was left in the book by someone. ✗
- The baby was born yesterday by its mother. ✗

D. Check the sentences if they can be written in the passive voice. If not, put a cross. Then rewrite the checked sentences in the passive voice.

Sentences that can be written in the passive voice:

1. Hannah will see the new action movie.
2. Someone stole my neighbour's car last night.
3. Nobody can solve the riddle within a minute.
4. The judge sentenced the criminal to two years in jail.

Rewritten Sentences in the Passive Voice:

( ) ____________________

( ) ____________________

( ) ____________________

Words that I Have Learned

____

____

____

Section 2 Grammar

UNIT 9

Direct and Indirect Speech

Direct speech repeats the exact words spoken; these words are put between quotation marks.

Indirect speech reports what someone else said; no quotation marks are needed.

Examples

- Mrs. Martin said to Paul, "You can take one." (direct)
- Mrs. Martin told Paul that he could take one. (indirect)

A. Identify each sentence. Write "D" for direct speech and "I" for indirect speech.

1. Ted explained, "The moon revolves around the Earth." ☐
2. "I like the cotton dress more," said Mabel. ☐
3. "I will attend the ceremony," said Fred's father. ☐
4. Karen always says that she is not good at singing. ☐
5. Jemima told Eric that the plan was impossible. ☐
6. Ivan says, "I always enjoy shopping with them." ☐
7. The waiter said that they did not have any cheesecake left. ☐
8. "We've tried many ways," Evelyn said to Mr. Wayne. ☐
9. Danika's friend screamed at her to duck. ☐
10. The paper boy apologized to Mrs. Ross that he had run out of newspapers. ☐

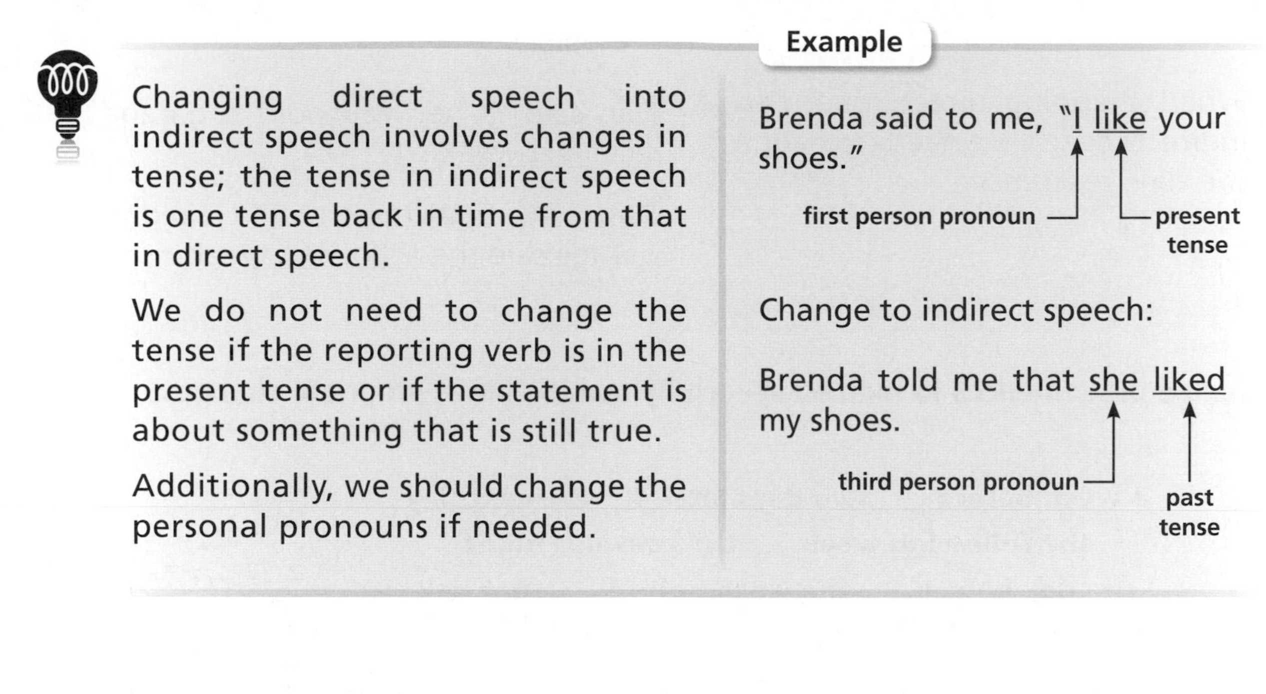

B. Change the sentences from direct speech to indirect speech.

1.  Clarissa said, "Nobody told me about the surprise party."

   ____

2. 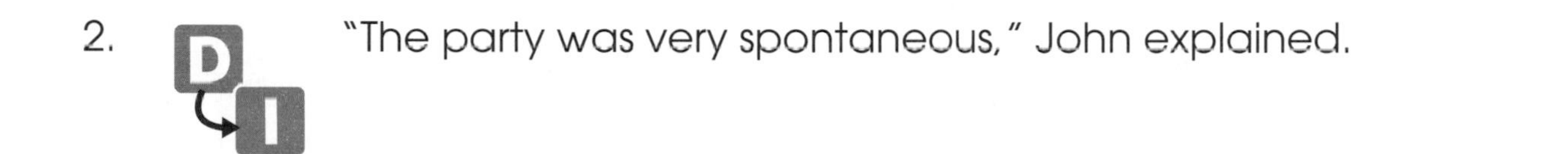 "The party was very spontaneous," John explained.

   ____

3.  Melody said, "That movie makes me cry."

   ____

4. "I do not need that," the woman replies.

   ____

5.  "I don't know where it is!" my little brother yells.

   ____

6.  "We are having a great time," the children said.

   ____

When changing direct speech to indirect speech, we need to change the time reference.

Example

Dan said, "They will hold a garage sale next week."

Dan said that they would hold a garage sale the following week.

C. Change the sentences to indirect speech by making the appropriate changes.

a week before **two days later** **the next day**
the following week **the previous night**
the day before **the week before** **that day**

1. "I didn't play in the game yesterday," Alex told his dad.

___

2. "It happened a week ago," said Ron.

___

3. The waiter said, "We are serving fresh seafood today."

___

4. "You have to tell me tomorrow," Brandon told Ginny.

___

5. "Grandma will come the day after tomorrow," said Molly.

___

6. Stan told Mr. Will, "My dog ate my homework last night."

___

7. The teacher told the class, "We will have an outing next week."

___

8. "They went to Hamilton last week," said Bill.

___

Changing direct questions to indirect questions:

- The tense in indirect questions is one tense back in time from that in direct questions.
- There is no need to use "Do/Does/Did".
- Change "Yes/No" questions by using "ask if/whether".

D. Change the questions to indirect speech.

1. "Which is the one you want?" Mrs. Watson asked Ben.

2. "Did you come from that way?" the police officer asked.

3. The lady asked the cashier, "How much do I owe?"

4. "What is your name?" Angela asked the boy.

5. Mrs. Healey asked the children, "Have you seen my cat?"

Words that I Have Learned

UNIT 10

The Mood of Sentences

The **mood** of a sentence tells us in what manner the verb is communicating the action. There are three types of mood: indicative mood, imperative mood, and subjunctive mood.

Examples

- We will have pizza for lunch tomorrow. (indicative)
- Please pass the salt. (imperative)
- I wish I could fly. (subjunctive)

A. Read the sentences. Identify the mood the sentences are in. Write the sentence numbers in the boxes.

1. Can you tell Jane not to disturb us while we are working?
2. It is a group project that accounts for 30% of the final score.
3. Go to the library to borrow some books for the project.
4. Matt has not finished compiling the data yet.
5. How I wish we had more time for the project.
6. Please bring all the materials we need.
7. If I were you, I would be done working on this project.
8. Group A will present their project first.
9. Would you please speak in front of the class?

Indicative Mood

- used to make a statement or ask a question

Imperative Mood

- used to make a command or request

Subjunctive Mood

- used to set up a hypothetical case or express a wish

We use the **subjunctive mood** to indicate a wish, a hypothetical case, a suggestion, or a demand.

Examples

- If I <u>were</u> the coach, I would not let him end the game.
  (Unfortunately, I am not the coach so I could not stop him.)
- If he <u>were</u> with us, it would be a lot more fun.
  (But he was not with us.)
- The teacher suggested that he <u>think</u> about it before getting back to her.
- Her mother demanded that she <u>stay</u> at home because she was sick.

Note the use of "were" in indicating wishes and hypothetical cases, and the use of the base verb in making suggestions or demands.

B. Fill in the blanks with the correct verbs to reflect the subjunctive mood.

Verbs

were **pay** **would** **book** **move**

You can use a verb more than once.

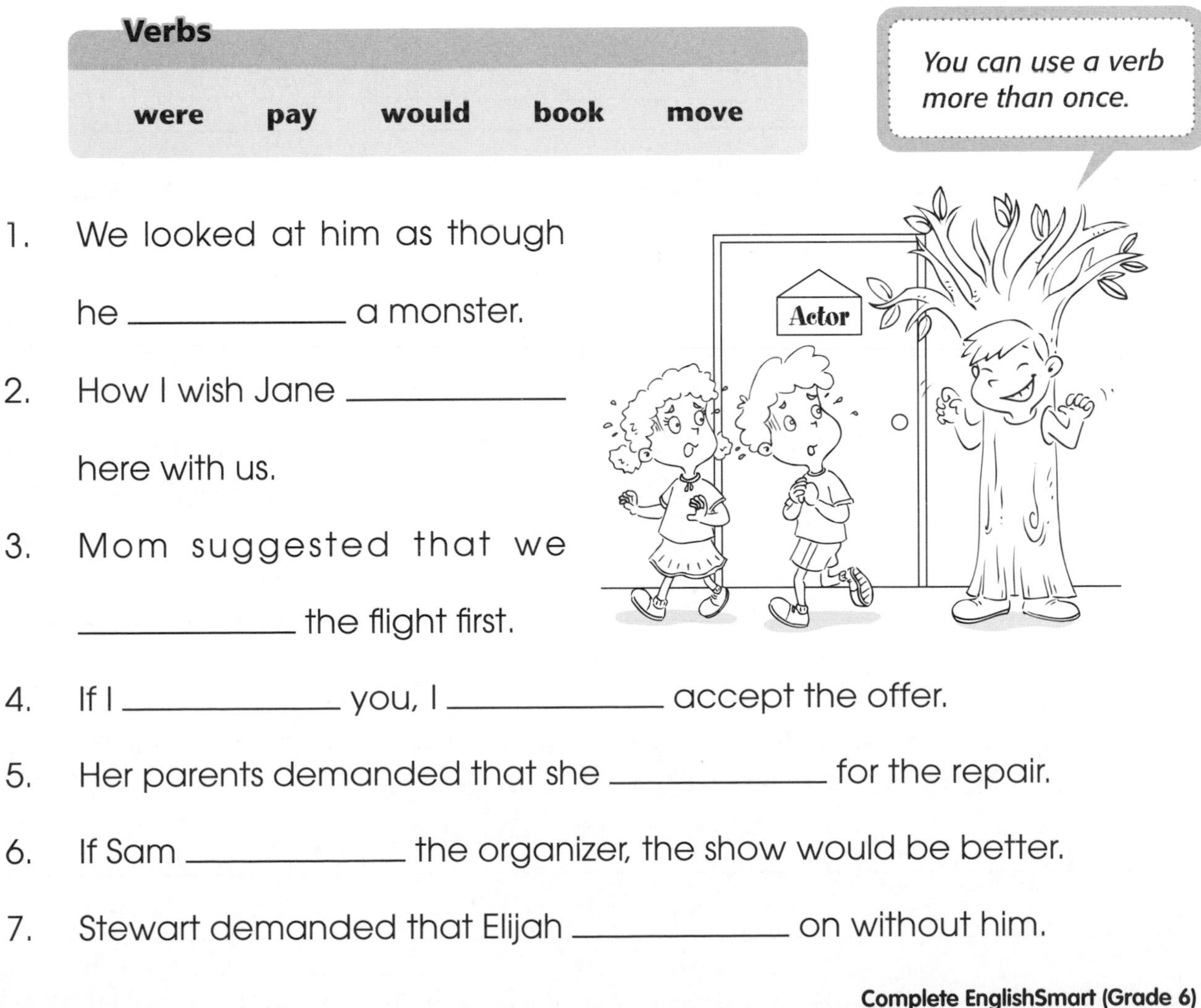

1. We looked at him as though he __________ a monster.
2. How I wish Jane __________ here with us.
3. Mom suggested that we __________ the flight first.
4. If I __________ you, I __________ accept the offer.
5. Her parents demanded that she __________ for the repair.
6. If Sam __________ the organizer, the show would be better.
7. Stewart demanded that Elijah __________ on without him.

C. Write a sentence in the subjunctive mood to show the main idea of each group of sentences.

Example

On the night of the show, Danika walked around making demands and ordering people. She acted like she was the star.

On the night of the show, Danika made so many requests as if she were the star of the show.

1. Damon knew who broke the vase. His mom asked him who did it but Damon pretended he was clueless.

____

____

2. Valerie was busy with her project. It was past midnight but there was a lot to do. Valerie's mom told her to leave it until the next day.

____

____

3. Jeremy was rude to Patricia. The teacher knew about it. She wanted Jeremy to apologize to Patricia.

____

____

4. Debbie went to an amusement park with her parents. She wanted to ride on the roller coaster, but her dad told her she was not tall enough. She was very disappointed.

____

____

5. Mr. Sherwood wants to stay fit. The doctor tells him to get up earlier and exercise for half an hour before going to work.

____

____

D. Write a sentence of your own for each.

Indicative Mood

Statement: ____________________

____

Question: ____________________

____

Imperative Mood

Command: ____________________

____

Request: ____________________

____

Subjunctive Mood

Hypothetical Case: ____________________

____

Wish: ____________________

____

Words that I Have Learned

____

____

____

UNIT 11

Clauses

Clauses can be independent or dependent.

An **independent clause** can stand on its own with a complete meaning.

A **dependent clause** cannot stand on its own and needs an independent clause to make its meaning complete.

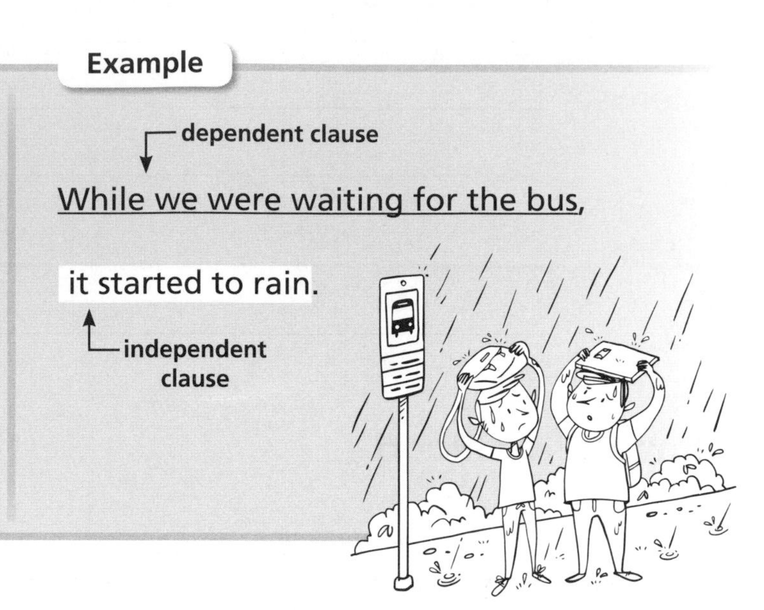

A. Circle to identify the independent clause (I) and the dependent clause (D).

1. he gave me an apple — I / D
2. while Darren sang the anthem — I / D
3. everyone thought it was funny — I / D
4. if the new girl is nice — I / D
5. Mr. Jenkins called me to his office — I / D
6. Aaron's lunch was delicious — I / D
7. before I continue — I / D
8. my friends and I laughed — I / D
9. when Ruben called — I / D
10. Riley was home alone — I / D
11. we cannot help wondering — I / D

An **independent clause** has a subject and a verb, and expresses a complete thought.

A **dependent clause** starts with a conjunction or a transition word and does not express a complete thought.

Examples

- Independent Clause: Jake quit his job
- Dependent Clause: before Jake quit his job

B. Draw a line to separate the independent clause from the dependent clause in each sentence. Write "I" or "D" above each to identify the type of clause.

e.g. Although it was late, | they continued to work on the project.
(D above "Although it was late,"; I above "they continued to work on the project.")

1. Wherever she goes, she carries her doll with her.
2. As I was going home, I saw Beth's little cousin.
3. If she had asked more politely, I would have agreed to help.
4. They gave up because there was too little time.
5. However hard they tried, they could not make it.
6. I would definitely go with you if I knew he was there.
7. Because the weather was so bad, we cancelled the trip.
8. If you want to succeed, you must put in effort and persevere.
9. She walks her dog when she has nothing better to do.

C. Complete each sentence by adding an independent clause to the dependent clause or a dependent clause to the independent clause. Write the new sentence.

The dependent clause can come before or after the independent clause. If it comes before it, add a comma after the dependent clause.

Dependent Clause , Independent Clause

1. his father was very pleased

2. whenever I am free

3. he did not show up

4. there was an uproar

5. she would not give in

6. as they were chatting

7. wherever he goes

8. I will make a deal with you

9. although we have never met before

10. because they lost their way

D. **Read the paragraph. Then underline the independent clauses and put the dependent clauses in parentheses ( ).**

Lucy and the Painting

It was Lucy's mom's birthday and Lucy wanted to buy her the perfect gift. Lucy was running out of time though since the surprise party was only a couple of days away. She thought about buying her mom a necklace but she already had many necklaces. She thought about buying her a dress but her mom already had too many. Lucy sat on her bed thinking about what her mom needed that she did not already have. After much thought, Lucy finally had an idea. Her worries were all gone when she remembered what her mom always told her. Whenever Lucy found it hard to get a gift for a friend, her mom would say, "The best gift comes from the heart." So although Lucy was not a great painter, she made a painting of herself and her mom together. It was her mom's favourite gift ever.

UNIT 12

Sentences

A **compound sentence** is made up of two or more independent clauses connected by conjunctions.

Example

We looked up at the night sky (independent clause) **and** (conjunction) there were countless stars (independent clause).

A. Circle the correct conjunction to complete the compound sentences.

1. The children could go to the zoo **but / or** they could have a picnic at the beach.
2. Dad will take a business trip to Vancouver next Tuesday **but / and** Mom will go with him.
3. Mrs. Wilson put the candles on the cake **and / or** the children sang the birthday song together.
4. Sarah wanted to win the tournament **but / and** she injured her shoulder last week.
5. James loves video games **or / but** he knows he cannot buy them all.
6. The team won the game **and / but** the coach was really pleased.
7. Tanya and Jim can buy a kitten **but / or** they can buy two hamsters.
8. Noelle and Marie want to dress up for Halloween **and / but** they have no idea what to wear yet.
9. Clara can wear the blue dress **and / or** she can wear a suit.

A **complex sentence** is made up of an independent clause with at least one dependent clause.

Example

Although it was raining heavily, (dependent clause)

the game continued. (independent clause)

B. Check the complex sentences and underline the dependent clauses in them. Put a cross for those that are not complex sentences.

1. Since it was Alex's birthday, Marjorie brought him a cake. ○

2. While I was waiting, I finished reading a very good book. ○
3. Although she did not tell me, I knew there was something wrong. ○
4. Jerry wanted ice cream and Carla wanted jelly, but Nellie preferred something hot. ○
5. Everything went well and the plane departed on schedule. ○
6. Peter does not give up even though he has failed three times already. ○
7. The Parkers had a relaxing stay in the mountains since the scenery there was breathtaking. ○
8. Do you think you can do it on your own or do you need my help? ○
9. If Annie's grandparents come to visit this summer, she will visit the aquarium with them. ○

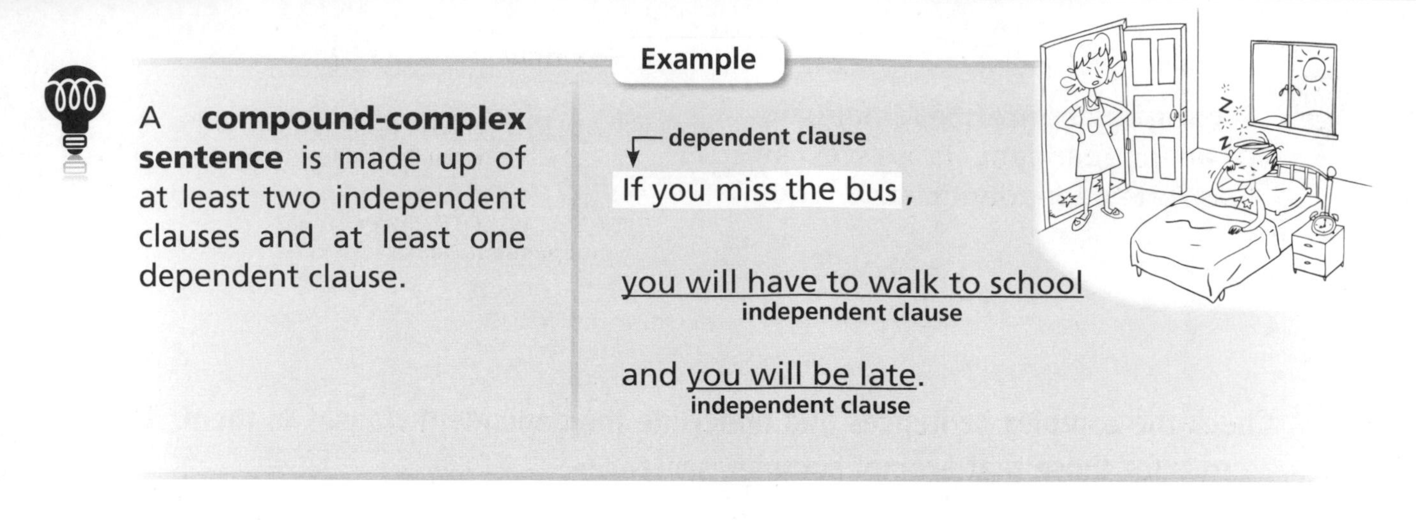

C. Create compound-complex sentences with the given clauses.

1.
- he was thrilled
- when he heard the news
- he ran upstairs to tell his father

2.
- if it rains
- we can watch a video at Jason's place
- we will not go to the park

3.
- she always makes friends
- Rosa is such a kind person
- wherever she goes

4.
- Lily carried boxes from the car
- Kate arranged the furniture
- while I painted the room

Compound-complex Sentence

1. ______________________________

2. ______________________________

3. ______________________________

4. ______________________________

D. Complete the compound, complex, and compound-complex sentences.

Compound Sentence

1. They arrived early but ______________________________ .
2. We can start all over again or ______________________________ .
3. The waiter did not say a word and ______________________________ .

Complex Sentence

4. We were told to stay indoors ______________________________ .
5. Although no one won the prize, ______________________________ .
6. I will go ahead with the project ______________________________ .

Compound-complex Sentence

7. While the girls were packing the room, ______________________________
______________________________ .
8. It was a sunny day ______________________________
______________________________ .
9. Since Dennis is going to Korea next year, ______________________________
______________________________ .

Words that I Have Learned

____

____

____

UNIT 13

Punctuation

Examples

We use a **comma** to:

- separate words or phrases in a series.
- separate adjectives before a noun.
- separate a dependent clause from an independent clause when the dependent clause appears first in the sentence.
- follow transition words.
- set off a direct quotation.
- set off words in apposition.

Examples:

- I enjoy playing hockey**,** baseball**,** and basketball.
- She wore a long**,** satin dress for the party.
- When they heard the news**,** they broke into tears.
- However**,** I ignored him and continued my work.
- Jeremy said to him**,** "You'd better finish it on time."
- Our teacher**,** Mr. Clark**,** will teach at another school.

A. Put commas in the correct places.

1. The storm left the village with flooded basements fallen trees and mudslides.
2. Our nanny Stefanie got a new job.
3. Although I did not see it happen I could feel the horror.
4. The incident happened on June 19 2004.
5. Vera put on her shiny diamond tiara for the ball last night.
6. The little boy replied "I just asked for some candies."
7. Consequently the student will have to redo the test.
8. Did you see the sleek blue sports car on the highway?
9. Once we start we should continue and not give up.

We also use **commas** to set off a non-defining clause in a sentence. A non-defining clause is one that adds information but is not a necessary part of the sentence.

Example

The coach, who is from Windsor, does not think that they stand a chance in the play-off.
(who is from Windsor = non-defining clause)

B. Check the sentences that have non-defining clauses. Then add comma(s) in the correct places.

1. The teachers who play in the game will practise tomorrow at the gym. ____
2. The show that he wanted to watch was not telecast. ____
3. Our dog which everyone loves likes eating treats. ____
4. Don't you want to be someone that everybody admires? ____
5. She let me see her camera which was as thin as a credit card. ____
6. Never trust a stranger who offers you a ride home. ____
7. He is a player whom everyone looks up to. ____
8. The tools that we need for the repair work are stored in the shed over there. ____
9. Pam's younger sister who looks very much like her will come to the party too. ____
10. I know a place where we can play hide-and-seek. ____
11. Mrs. Steele whose son is about my age bakes great cookies. ____

Section 2 Grammar

Examples

We use a **colon**:

- to introduce a list of items or a quotation.
- to set off a concluding statement.
- between a title and a subtitle.
- between two clauses when the second one explains the first.

- There are three main ingredients in lemon squares**:** lemon juice, sugar, and flour.
- When you are travelling, remember one thing**:** home is where the heart is.
- The writers agreed that "The Best Word**:** The Art of Writing Well" was worth a second read.
- There are two ways you can get to the island**:** you can take a boat or you can take an airplane.

C. Check if the colons are in the right places. If not, cross them out and add the colons in the correct places in red.

1. The chairman neglected one crucial fact: the report was not ready. _____
2. The article "Travel in Asia China and India": is an interesting read. _____
3. We expect only one thing from him complete the project: by next Monday. _____
4. Do remember: this never ever give up. _____
5. We all have the same goal win the tournament: this time. _____
6. The old saying goes: "Blood is thicker than water." _____
7. She was told to pack these for the trip: a flashlight, a compass, and water. _____

We use a **semicolon**:

- in place of a conjunction to join two closely related clauses or sentences.
- between a series of items when the items are long or contain commas within.

Examples

- It is raining today**;** we will go to the zoo another day.
- Danielle has three favourite books: "The Secret Garden"**;** "The Lion, the Witch and the Wardrobe"**;** "The Witches".

D. Add semicolons in the correct places. Then look at the picture and write a sentence that contains a semicolon about it.

1. He was introduced to the following people: Jason, Peter's cousin Mandy, his boss's daughter Sam, the secretary's husband.
2. It was chilly out there the temperature dropped to a mere 2°C.
3. They met with John it was a brief meeting.
4. No one wanted to leave they were all eager for the announcement.
5. She is such a popular athlete wherever she goes, she is surrounded by fans.

My Sentence

Words that I Have Learned

Section 2 Grammar

UNIT 14 More on Punctuation

We use a **dash** to:

- separate a series at the beginning of a sentence from its explanatory section.
- set off a description or comment that is meant to further the reader's understanding of the sentence.
- set off an elaboration of an idea at the end of a sentence.

Examples

- A compass, a radio, and a watch – these are the essentials we need for a hike.
- The science project – the most difficult of all – will account for 40% of the total score.
- They had only one thing in mind – winning the game.

A. Add dashes with "^" where needed.

1. The final showdown –^ the do-or-die game will be telecast live.
2. Everything boiled down to one word perseverance.
3. *The Greatest Game Ever Played* the story of an underdog golfer is the best motivational film I have ever watched.
4. Apples, pears, and melons these are the fruits we need for the salad.
5. I should tell her the truth I was the one who accidentally lost her necklace.
6. The one rule they had to not speak loudly was not followed.
7. No matter what you do explain, plead, or beg it will not change her mind.

We use a **hyphen** to form compound words, divide a word into syllables, or indicate a split in a word at the end of a line.

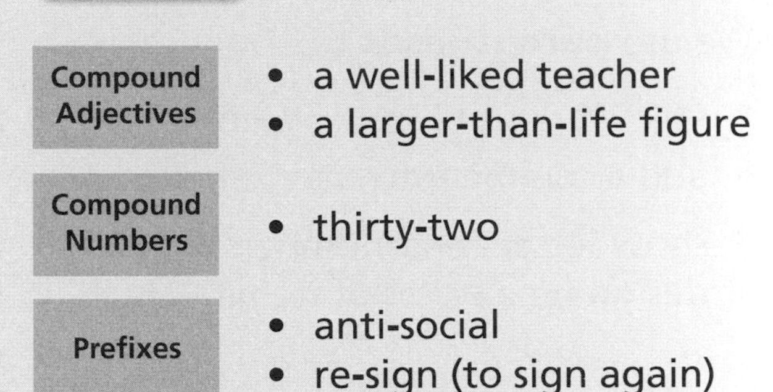

Examples

Compound Adjectives	• a well-liked teacher • a larger-than-life figure
Compound Numbers	• thirty-two
Prefixes	• anti-social • re-sign (to sign again)

B. Rewrite the sentences adding hyphens where needed.

1. The new manager is a twenty three year old graduate.

____

2. This is a once in a lifetime chance that you should not miss.

____

3. He lives in a twenty six year old split level bungalow.

____

4. Jordan's mother in law came to visit them for two weeks.

____

5. The school exams will be from mid November to mid December.

____

6. Many people were inspired by his from rags to riches story.

____

____

7. Elisa's research shows that two thirds of the population is under fifty five years of age.

____

____

Examples

We use **parentheses** to:

- enclose additional information.
- add a comment to a statement.
- show letters and numbers that designate a series of items.

- The Mennonites **(**with a dwindling population**)** reside mainly in St. Jacobs, Ontario.
- California **(**see Figure 2**)** is an American state along the Pacific Ocean.
- Before leaving, remember to **(**a**)** switch off all the lights, **(**b**)** close all the windows, and **(**c**)** lock the door.

C. Check if the sentences are using parentheses correctly. If not, add parentheses in the correct places.

1. The supporting role Captain Truman was given to a little-known actor by the name of (Willie Whitt). ____

2. The new museum (see insert) will be officially opened on Monday. ____

3. The honour students of which I am one are invited (to the ceremony). ____

4. The complimentary tickets (a pair from Uncle Charlie and another pair from Mr. Todd) came just in time. ____

5. The students should a (get a form), b (fill it out), c (get their parents' consent), and d (return it to their teacher before noon tomorrow). ____

6. The graph Fig. 2b shows (the population growth) over the past 20 years. ____

7. The series (2-2) would be decided in the final game to be played this afternoon. ____

8. The merger yet to be confirmed (is set to take effect) in January next year. ____

We use **ellipsis dots** to shorten a quotation when the quotation is longer than what we need.

Example

It is stated clearly in Clause 3:

"...with the consent of the director and three board members."

D. Add ellipsis dots with "^" where needed.

e.g. A Great White ranges from five to seven metres in length ... swimming at a speed of 16 to 20 km per hour, the Great White usually attacks its prey from behind or beneath.

1. Roberta Bondar became the first female astronaut to go into space. She received the Order of Canada Roberta was named to the Canadian Medical Hall of Fame in 1998.

2. There are many ways to conserve energy more and more people switch to driving small cars which are more fuel efficient.

3. Smart phones are becoming so dangerous for people, for example, some people forget to look both ways before crossing a street that some organizations are promoting safe smart phone use and habits.

4. Recent research indicates that most of the asteroids orbit the sun the chance of an asteroid striking the Earth is one in a million.

Words that I Have Learned

____

____

____

A. Circle the answers.

1. Which sentence has the adverb underlined?

   Daniella lovingly looked at her son.

   Duff hungrily gobbled everything.

   Dan slept peacefully on the sofa.

2. What type of pronoun is underlined in the sentence below?

   Can anybody help me?

   an object pronoun

   a relative pronoun

   an indefinite pronoun

3. Which sentence contains an irregular verb?

   I taught chemistry for many years.

   I loved to dance in the rain.

   I laughed at my brother.

4. Which verb tense is formed with "will + be + -ing form of a verb"?

   present progressive tense

   past progressive tense

   future progressive tense

5. What type of verbal is underlined in the sentence below?

   The man carried a walking stick.

   a gerund

   a participle

   an infinitive

6. A gerund functions as a/an ______ .

   noun

   adjective

   adverb

7. What type of verbal phrase is underlined in the sentence below?

   He could not wait to see her!

   a participle phrase

   a gerund phrase

   an infinitive phrase

8. Which sentence has an adjective phrase underlined?

   The boy was wearing a blue shirt.

   The boy in the blue shirt cried.

   The blue shirt was put on the shelf.

9. Which sentence is written in the passive voice?

   Anne wrote the book.

   Anne was writing the book.

   The book was written by Anne.

10. The tense in indirect speech is ______ in time from that in direct speech.

    one tense back

    one tense forward

    not changed

11. Which sentence is in indirect speech of the sentence below?

Ron says, "I will swim tomorrow."

Ron said that he would swim tomorrow.

Ron says that he will swim the next day.

Ron said that he would swim the next day.

12. The ______ mood is used to express a wish.

indicative

imperative

subjunctive

13. The imperative mood is used to ______ .

make a statement

make a command

set up a hypothetical case

14. An independent clause ______ .

can stand on its own

cannot stand on its own

has an incomplete meaning

15. A "______" is added after a dependent clause if it comes before an independent clause.

16. What is used to connect the independent clauses in a compound sentence?

an interjection

a conjunction

a relative pronoun

17. What can a compound-complex sentence be made up of?

two or more independent clauses

one independent and one dependent clause

two independent clauses and one dependent clause

18. What punctuation is used between a title and a subtitle?

a dash

a colon

ellipsis dots

19. Parentheses are used to ______ .

enclose additional information

list a series of items

set off a direct quotation

20. What punctuation should be used in the circle below?

She is twenty ◯ two years old.

a dash

a hyphen

a semicolon

Parts of Speech

B. Write the numbers to put the underlined words in the correct boxes. Then circle the personal, indefinite, and relative pronouns with the specified colours.

As part of her summer (1) vacation, Rachel travelled (2) from Ottawa, Canada to Cushendall, Ireland. She stayed with her Aunt Anne and Uncle Pat (3) for three weeks. They (4) lived in a large house in the (5) rolling countryside. (6) It was her first time in Ireland and she did not know what to expect.

When Rachel arrived, she exclaimed, "(7) Wow! This place is beautiful!" It was a warm and (8) sunny day. Rachel was eager to play outside (9) but she had to unpack her things (10) neatly first. As she was unpacking, she was introduced to someone whom she had never met before. It was Murphy, her aunt and uncle's Golden Retriever. He was very (11) friendly with them and soon (12) started following Rachel around. (13) After Rachel had finished unpacking, she went outside to play (14) in the grass with Murphy.

Murphy discovered an old tree (15) stump and kept sniffing (16) curiously behind (17) it. Rachel went over to see what he had found. (18) Oh! It was something beyond her wildest imagination!

Part of Speech

Noun

Verb

Adjective

Adverb

Pronoun

Preposition

Conjunction

Interjection

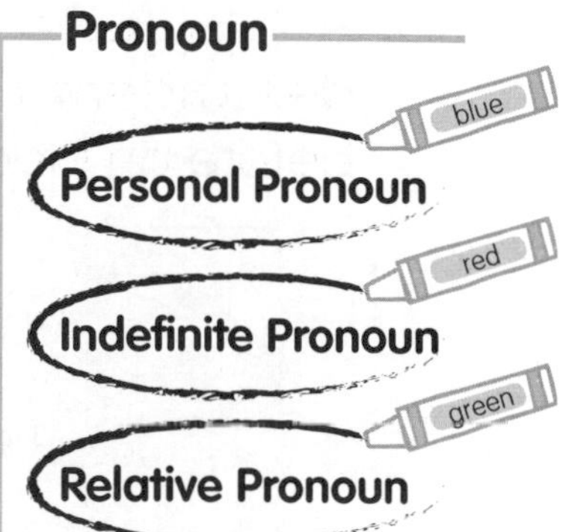

Verb Tenses, Verbals, and Verbal Phrases

C. Identify the verb tense of the underlined verb in each sentence. Write the sentence number in the box.

1. Rachel jumped in surprise to see a tiny man with red hair behind the stump.
2. He was staring back at her with equal surprise!
3. "He is so strange," Rachel thought.
4. "I'm a leprechaun," he introduced himself. "I will grant you three wishes."
5. "She will be thinking very carefully all afternoon about her wishes," he thought.
6. "I am wondering if I could have a giant cheesecake," Rachel said immediately.
7. To her surprise, a giant, gooey cheesecake appeared in front of her!
8. Rachel was devouring the cake when she realized that it was getting dark.

Simple Present

Simple Past

Simple Future

Future Progressive

D. Write the type of verbal each phrase contains. Then fill in the blanks with the correct verbal phrases. Write the letters.

Type of Verbal

A finding a leprechaun ________

B overwhelmed with excitement ________

C to get back to Aunt Anne's house ________

1. Rachel was eager ______ .
2. She realized that ______ was the best thing ever.
3. Therefore, ______, she quickly ran back to the house with the leprechaun in her pocket.

More on Phrases and Active and Passive Voice

E. Write "NP" for noun phrases, "Adj. P" for adjective phrases, and "Adv. P" for adverb phrases above the underlined phrases.

Rachel was greeted by a worried looking Aunt Anne. A delicious, mouth-watering dinner had been prepared for her. However, Rachel had to excuse herself and said, "I'm sorry but I'm not feeling well." Then she went upstairs.

When she got to her room, Rachel took the leprechaun, who had been sleeping quite soundly, out of her pocket. The leprechaun woke up and sat on the pillow. Rachel wanted the leprechaun to grant her second wish.

Although the leprechaun warned her to think about it carefully, Rachel was quick to say in an excited, high-pitched voice, "I already know that I want a shiny red bike with a blue bell on its handlebar." The leprechaun granted Rachel's wish and a bike appeared out of thin air!

F. Circle "A" if the sentences are in the active voice; circle "P" if they are in the passive voice.

1. The bike was quietly carried downstairs and hidden in the shed by Rachel at night. **A / P**
2. Rachel, Murphy, and the leprechaun slept peacefully. **A / P**

3. In the morning, Rachel placed the leprechaun in her pocket. **A / P**
4. Rachel rode her bike to the library. **A / P**
5. The bike was locked carelessly in front of the library. **A / P**

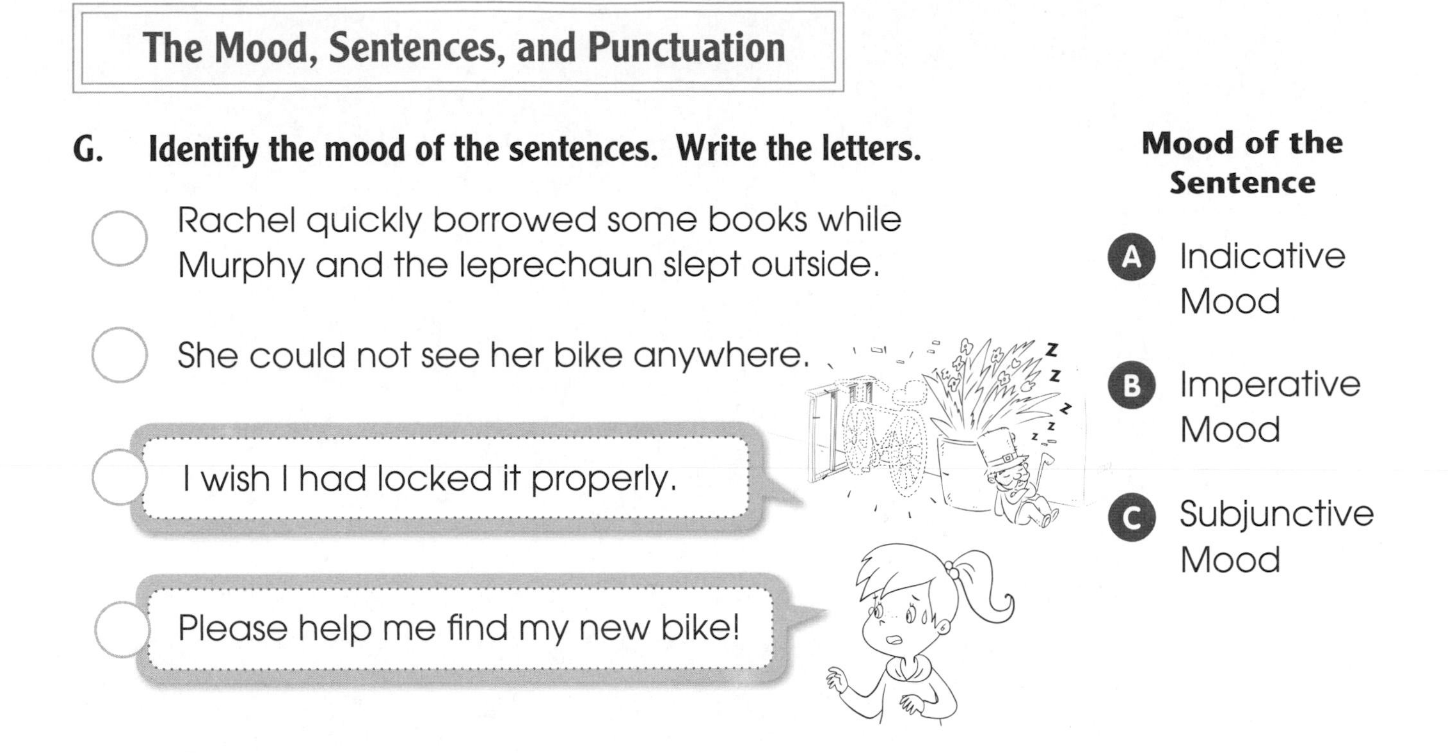

The Mood, Sentences, and Punctuation

G. Identify the mood of the sentences. Write the letters.

Mood of the Sentence

- **A** Indicative Mood
- **B** Imperative Mood
- **C** Subjunctive Mood

( ) Rachel quickly borrowed some books while Murphy and the leprechaun slept outside.

( ) She could not see her bike anywhere.

( ) I wish I had locked it properly.

( ) Please help me find my new bike!

H. Write "compound", "complex", or "compound-complex" above each underlined sentence. Then add dashes, hyphens, parentheses, and ellipsis dots where needed.

Rachel was desperate to find her new bike she had never been this attached to anything before. She considered the following options: 1 look for the thief herself, 2 post flyers everywhere, and 3 use her third wish to find her bike.

Rachel weighed her options and she picked the third one. She said to the leprechaun, "For my third wish, I want to know who took my bike."

After he made sure Rachel's third wish was well thought out, the leprechaun smiled and he told her to look around the corner.

When she peeked around the corner, Rachel saw a boy with her bike! He explained that he lost his bike the day before and he found it just then. The leprechaun attempted to explain, "I did warn you to think carefully"

Before he could say anything else, Rachel hugged him. She was happy because nothing could be better than meeting a wish granting leprechaun in the first place!

Section 3

Vocabulary

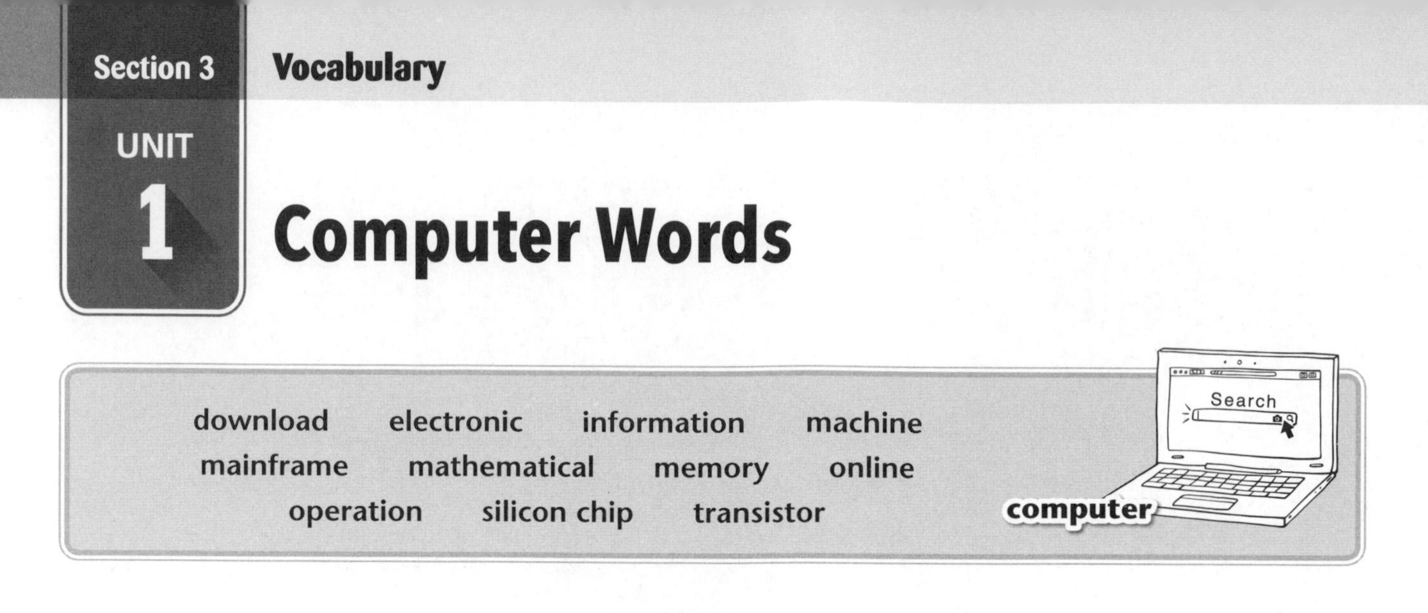

UNIT 1

Computer Words

download electronic information machine
mainframe mathematical memory online
operation silicon chip transistor

No More Pencils...No More Books

A familiar "end of year" chant for schoolchildren begins with the words, "No more pencils, no more books". Could this also be a prophecy? Will the age of computer technology advance to the stage where books and pencils become obsolete in schools?

Before considering these questions, it is useful to reflect on the history of the computer. Its roots go back to 1822 when an Englishman by the name of Charles Babbage created a computation machine. Recognizing the need for storing information primarily mathematical in nature, Babbage attempted to develop a machine powered by a steam engine to store information on punch cards. Babbage's concept was sound but the technology available was inadequate to meet the task at hand.

The first electronic computer produced by the US Army in 1946 was named the ENIAC (Electronic Numerical Integrator And Computer). It weighed 30 tons and took up enough floor space to fill a normal-sized house. It was capable of performing about 5000 operations per second but because it produced enormous amounts of heat while in operation, it had to be shut down regularly to cool off.

Advancements in computer technology can be recorded in four principal generations. The first would be the mainframe format such as the ENIAC. With the invention of the transistor, the second generation of smaller, faster, and less expensive computers came on the scene. By 1996, the miniature integrated circuits took the place of transistors, creating the new wave of computers with expanded memory capabilities, operating at relatively high speeds. Finally, the silicon chip marked the fourth generation of computers. These were smaller, faster, and cheaper, initiating the beginning of the PC (personal computer).

Imagine a future where every school is virtual. Instead of the teacher taking attendance, students simply log on from home, and instead of reading textbooks, students learn everything online. Students can download their lessons and all communications can be done through e-mail. Would you like that kind of future?

A. Circle the correct computer words for the definitions.

1. performed or done using the Internet

   transistor   online   operation

2. a very large and powerful computer

   mainframe   silicon chip   memory

3. a step performed in the execution of a program on a computer

   information   operation   electronic

4. transfer data from a website to one's computer

   download   machine   transistor

5. a piece of equipment involving different parts to perform a specific task

   online   operation   machine

6. the capacity for storing information

   memory   transistor   silicon chip

7. of or related to mathematics

   information   electronic   mathematical

8. an electronic device that stores and processes information

   computer

   memory

   operation

Section 3
Vocabulary

B. Fill in the blanks with the correct computer words.

More Computer Words

blog **firewall** **gigabytes** **app** **pasted** **USB flash drive**
browser **virus** **password** **junk mail** **uploaded**

1. Jamie's favourite ________________ is Instagram because he loves photography.

2. Lydia updated her web ________________ so it will be faster.

3. The student copied and ________________ the lesson from her e-mail to a document file.

4. Sean set up a ________________ on his new laptop so he will not get a ________________ .

5. Gina's new smart phone only has eight ________________ of memory, but she thinks it is already enough for her.

6. Food and Fashion is Kylie's favourite ________________ and Jensen Little is her favourite blogger.

7. My cousin set up a new e-mail account because she received too much ________________ .

8. The thief easily guessed the ________________ to the man's computer.

9. My mom ________________ the pictures from the trip to the family group chat last night.

10. Vanessa transferred documents onto the ________________ from her computer.

C. **Identify the labelled parts in the diagram. Then research and write their uses.**

Computer Words

speaker web camera
monitor mouse
keyboard CPU

A ______________ : ______________________________

____

B ______________ : ______________________________

____

C ______________ : ______________________________

____

D ______________ : ______________________________

____

E ______________ : ______________________________

____

F ______________ : ______________________________

____

Words that I Have Learned

Computer Words

____

____

____

____

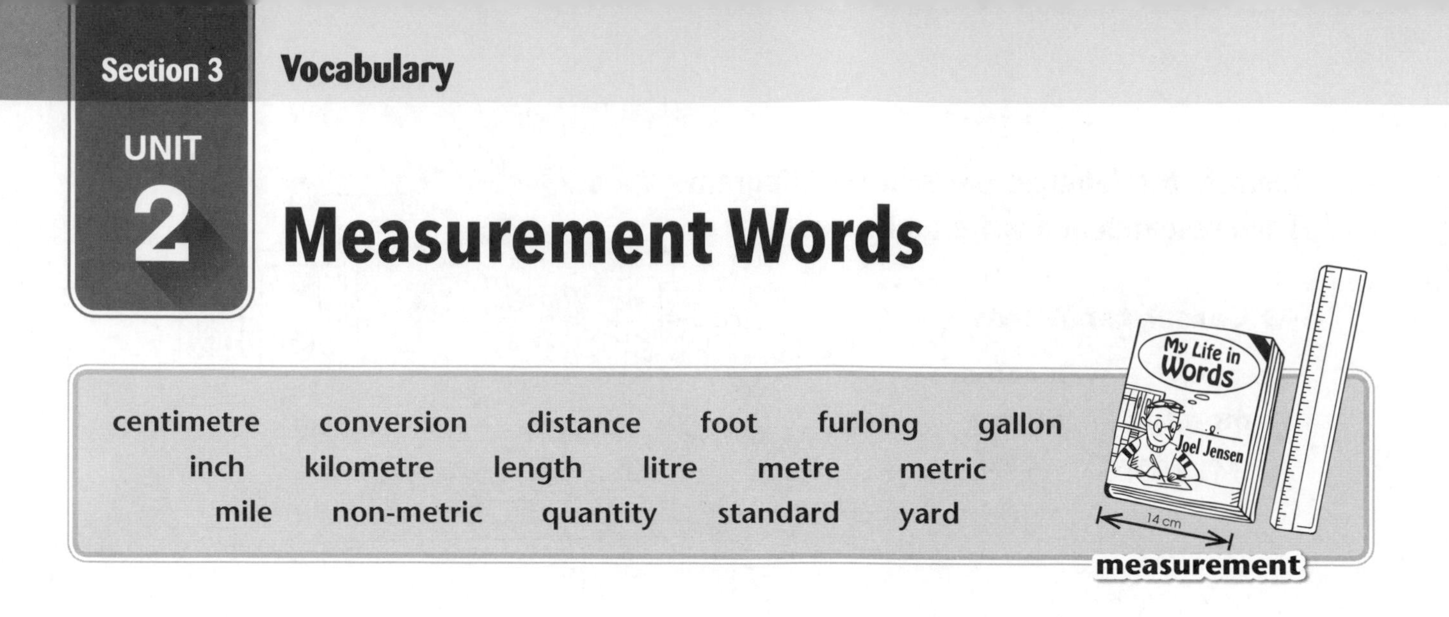

UNIT 2 Measurement Words

centimetre conversion distance foot furlong gallon
inch kilometre length litre metre metric
mile non-metric quantity standard yard

Accurate Measurement Was Not Always Accurate

While Canada and the United States share a common language and many aspects of culture are similar, they differ in the language of measurement. In the early 1970s, Canada started adopting the metric system of measurement widely used throughout Europe. Thus, inches were replaced by centimetres, yards by metres, miles by kilometres, and gallons by litres. By multiplying or dividing by 10, 100, or 1000, conversions between various lengths and quantities in the metric system are easily calculated.

Measurement, however, was not always so mathematically accurate. The foot, for example, was initially determined to be the length of a person's actual foot. The obvious problem with this measurement was the variety in length of the human foot. Therefore, the foot of a nobleman or leader was used to standardize the length.

The Romans are credited with establishing the first standard mile. Using the measurement of 5 Roman feet to measure a pace, that is one step, and 1000 paces to walk a mile, they determined that one mile would equal 5000 feet as it came to be known. However, this measurement was not acceptable in England because it did not conform to the measurement of 8 furlongs to a mile. A furlong, the common measurement used on farms, was 220 yards, and 8 furlongs (a mile) totalled 5280 feet – the distance that is used today. England's Henry I proclaimed that the yard should be the distance from his nose to the end of his thumb on his outstretched arm. Before Henry's declaration, the yard was the length of a girdle around the king's waist which would have increased greatly had they used the waistline of Henry VIII.

The British, who were the originators of this non-metric system still used by Americans today, also switched to the metric system to simplify the mathematics of measurement. For the Americans to follow suit would be a costly venture but one that would be embraced by schoolchildren.

A. **Match the measurement words with the facts and definitions. Write the letters in the circles.**

Measurement Word		Fact and Definition
A centimetres	◯	replaced gallons
B litres	◯	replaced miles
C metres	◯	8 furlongs or 5280 feet
D length	◯	5000 feet
E mile	◯	220 yards
F furlong	◯	the measurement of the longest part of something
G Roman mile	◯	a change from one form to another
H kilometres	◯	replaced yards
I conversion	◯	replaced inches

B. **Write the definition of each measurement word.**

inch: ______________________________

____

metric: ______________________________

____

distance: ______________________________

____

standard: ______________________________

____

I can help you!

Dictionary

Dictionary

C. Identify each unit of measurement as metric (M) or non-metric (NM). Write "M" or "NM" on the line.

1. centimetre ________
2. mile ________
3. acre ________
4. yard ________
5. kilogram ________
6. metre ________
7. inch ________
8. pound ________
9. gallon ________
10. litre ________
11. foot ________
12. kilometre ________
13. ounce ________
14. millilitre ________

D. Circle the units of measurement in the sentences.

1. Julia lives four kilometres away from school.
2. Navi's little sister was four feet tall on her tenth birthday.
3. The Smithsons own 12 acres of farmland in northern Ontario.
4. Chef Gulliani added three tablespoons of his secret spice mix to the vegetables.
5. In Canada, it can get as hot as 40 degrees Celsius.
6. Aunt Carey is always ten minutes late to every appointment.
7. It took Gisele 50 seconds to run from the tree to the fountain.
8. The movie finished two hours ago so they should be home by now.
9. I need 60 centimetres of ribbon for the bow.

E. **Fill in the blanks with the correct units of measurement.**

Units of Measurement

tablespoons **millilitres** **cup** **grams**
seconds **minute** **teaspoon**

Simple Pancake Recipe

Ingredients

- 1 ____________ of flour
- 2 ____________ of sugar
- 1 ____________ of salt
- 1 egg (beaten)
- 250 ____________ of milk
- 50 ____________ of butter (melted)

Steps

1. Mix ingredients in a bowl.
2. Add a ladle of butter into a frying pan on medium heat.
3. Cook for one ____________ . Then flip and cook for 30 ____________ .
4. Put on a plate and serve.

The final step is to pour maple syrup on top and enjoy!

Maple Syrup

Words that I Have Learned

Measurement Words

____

____

____

____

UNIT 3

Physical Activity Words

aerobic brisk challenge endurance
exhausting fitness injury marathon
rest stamina strength training

Running a Marathon

Running a marathon is the ultimate test of physical fitness. It is true that most people know how to run. Running a marathon, however, is quite a different challenge.

The official distance of a marathon run is 26 miles 385 yards (42 kilometres). In order to complete this distance, a runner, and certainly a novice runner, must prepare carefully. First, a person should get a physical check-up from his or her doctor to ensure that running such a long distance is safe. Once this is confirmed, training can begin. For a person who is a beginner runner, it takes a minimum of three months or, in most cases, much longer to properly train for a marathon. In addition to long hours of training, it is important that the runner avoids illness and injury.

Novice runners should begin with brisk, lengthy walks. Running can begin after a few weeks of regular walking sessions with increased speed and distance at consistent intervals. Training should involve running at least five days a week with a steady distance increase of 15 – 20% every two weeks. As training intensifies, longer runs should become part of the training. For example, it is suggested that a long run of 24 to 30 kilometres should become a regular part of training once the runner is getting close to the race day. It is also recommended that, to offset the longer training run, a short run (5 to 8 kilometres) one day a week be part of the routine, as well as one day of complete rest.

The marathon run is a gruelling, exhausting test of strength, stamina, and aerobic fitness. Anyone who completes the race, regardless of his or her overall final race standing, can be proud of having accomplished one of the most difficult tests of physical endurance.

A. Read the clues and complete the crossword puzzle with the physical activity words from the passage.

Across

- **A** the state of being fit and healthy
- **B** fast, energetic
- **C** relating to the body's ability to use oxygen
- **D** hurt or damage
- **E** something that needs great effort to be done
- **F** very tiring

Down

- **1** the ability and strength to sustain prolonged activity
- **2** the ability to withstand hardship
- **3** the state of being strong
- **4** a course of exercise or practice
- **5** the state of relaxation with minimal activity
- **6** a long distance running race

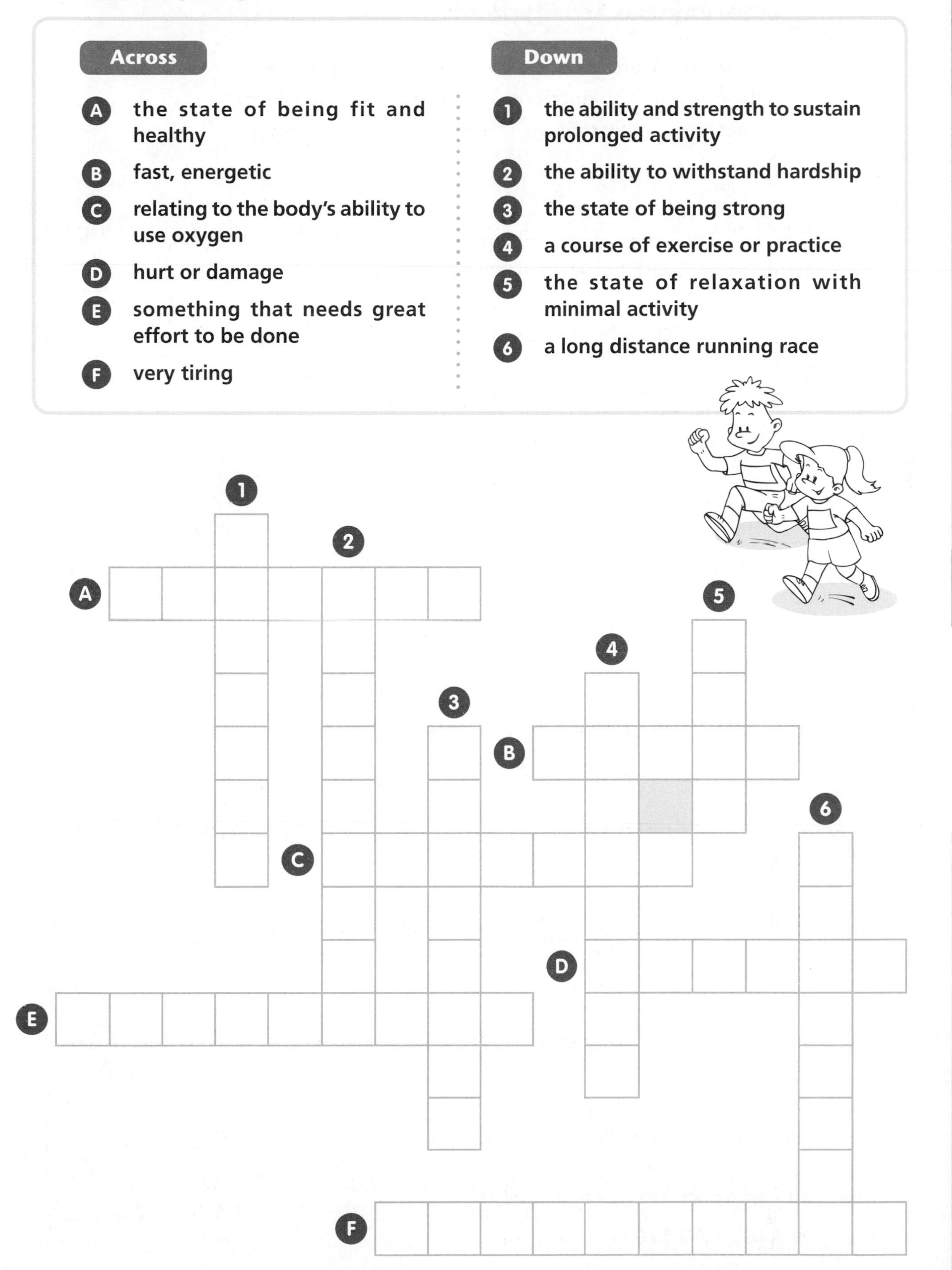

B. Fill in the blanks with the correct physical activity words.

More Physical Activity Words

motivation	muscles	judo	recovers
Kinesiology	nutrients	routine	healthful
active	stretching	physician	warm up

1. Emily maintains an ____________ lifestyle by joining sports teams, going to the gym, and doing outdoor activities.

2. Our gym teacher Ms. Guzman studied ____________ at Queen's University.

3. Kyle's favourite style of martial arts is ____________ .

4. Sometimes it is hard to find the ____________ to exercise.

5. My brother's ____________ were sore after his training last night.

6. Tina is going to see her family ____________ for her annual check-up.

7. It is important to eat fruits and vegetables because they have the ____________ our bodies need.

8. Rudy has to wait until he fully ____________ from his injury before practising again.

9. Angelina's trainer told her that jump rope is a good exercise to ____________ .

10. The personal trainer taught Cody his very own exercise ____________ .

11. Mrs. Evans feeds her kids only ____________ foods.

12. Besides increasing the body's flexibility, ____________ also helps release stress.

C. Label the diagram to show different types of exercises.

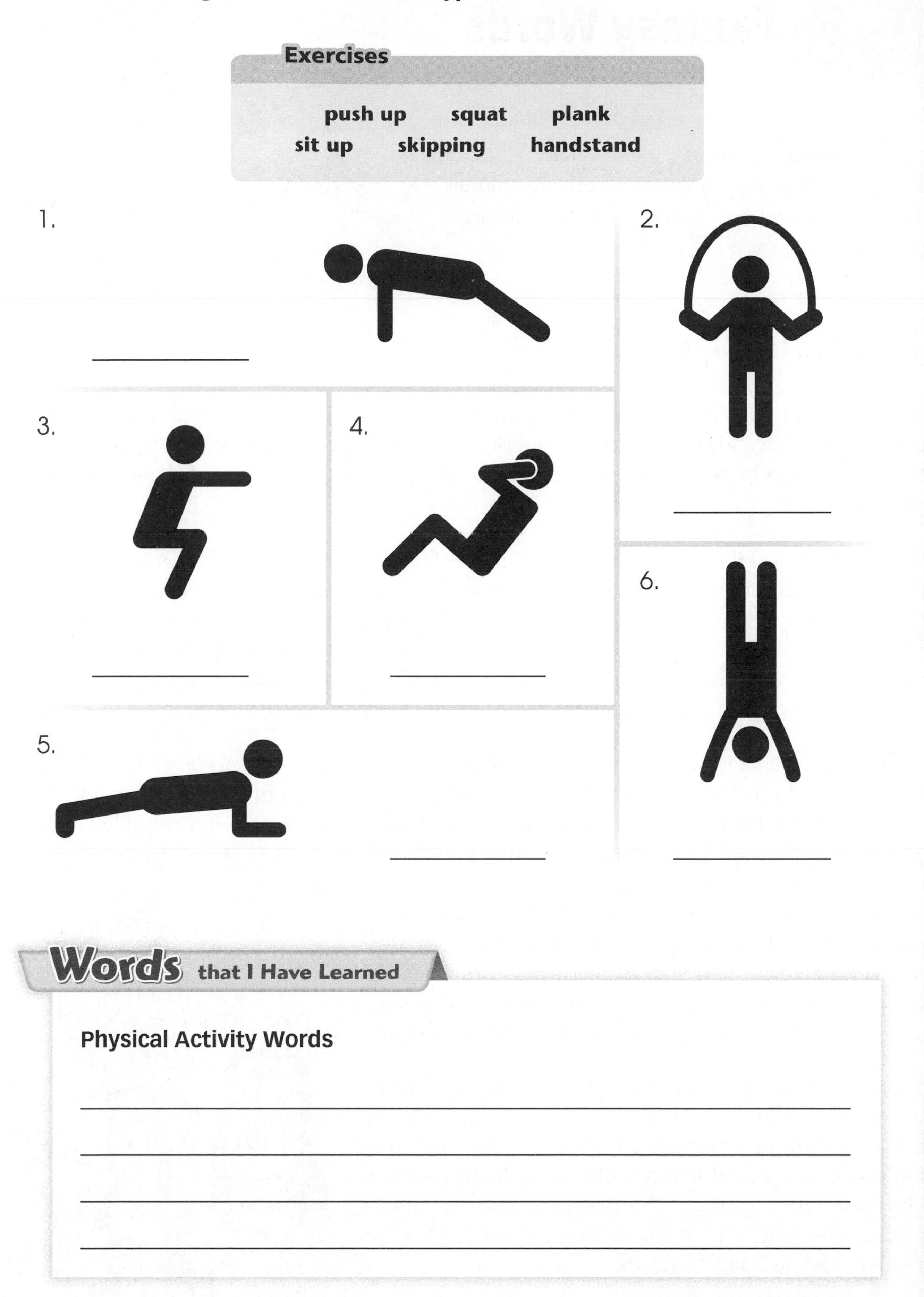

Words that I Have Learned

Physical Activity Words

UNIT 4

Fantasy Words

J. R. R. Tolkien

John Ronald Reuel Tolkien, commonly known as J. R. R. Tolkien, is a celebrated author, poet, philologist, and university professor. He published many works of fiction and non-fiction, but he is most famous for two of his novels titled *The Hobbit* and *The Lord of the Rings*.

The Hobbit is a children's fantasy novel that was first published in 1937. The story contains many mythical creatures, including elves, fairies, and dwarves. The main character in the novel is a creature known as a hobbit – a small, human-like creature with very hairy feet who never wears shoes. The story is about the hobbit Bilbo Baggins who goes on an adventure to win a portion of treasure guarded by a cruel dragon named Smaug. The novel achieved wide critical acclaim and is recognized as a classic in children's literature.

Following the success of *The Hobbit*, Tolkien wrote a sequel titled *The Lord of the Rings*. It is one of the bestselling novels ever written, with over 150 million copies sold. The novel is meant for an adult audience and is categorized as an epic fantasy novel. Like *The Hobbit*, this novel involves many mythical and heroic characters who must embark on an epic adventure across the fictional land of Middle-Earth. It follows the course of the war of the ring through the eyes of its main characters, including two men, one dwarf, one elf, four hobbits, and a wizard named Gandalf. The story also has terrifying monsters such as goblins and trolls.

Tolkien's writing has received enduring popularity in both scholarly and popular culture. His work has been adapted into comics, TV shows, music, and most famously, six award-winning films. Tolkien's work is credited with resurging the popularity of the fantasy genre, causing him to be known as the "father" of modern-day fantasy literature.

A. Write to match the fantasy words with their definitions.

Fantasy Words

fictional creature monster novel hobbit
dragon heroic goblin wizard fantasy

1. ______________________
a giant, mythical, winged reptile that breathes fire

2. ______________________
a small, human-like creature with hairy feet created by J. R. R. Tolkien

3. ______________________
imaginary, relating to fiction

4. ______________________
a genre of books containing unrealistic settings, mythical creatures, and magical events

5. ______________________
a large, ugly, frightening, imaginary creature

6. ______________________
a very clever man with magical powers in stories

7. ______________________
a mythical, imaginary being

8. ______________________
having the brave characteristics of heroes or heroines

9. ______________________
a small, ugly, imaginary creature that is usually mischievous

10. ______________________
a long, written story about imaginary characters and events

B. Identify and name the mythical creatures.

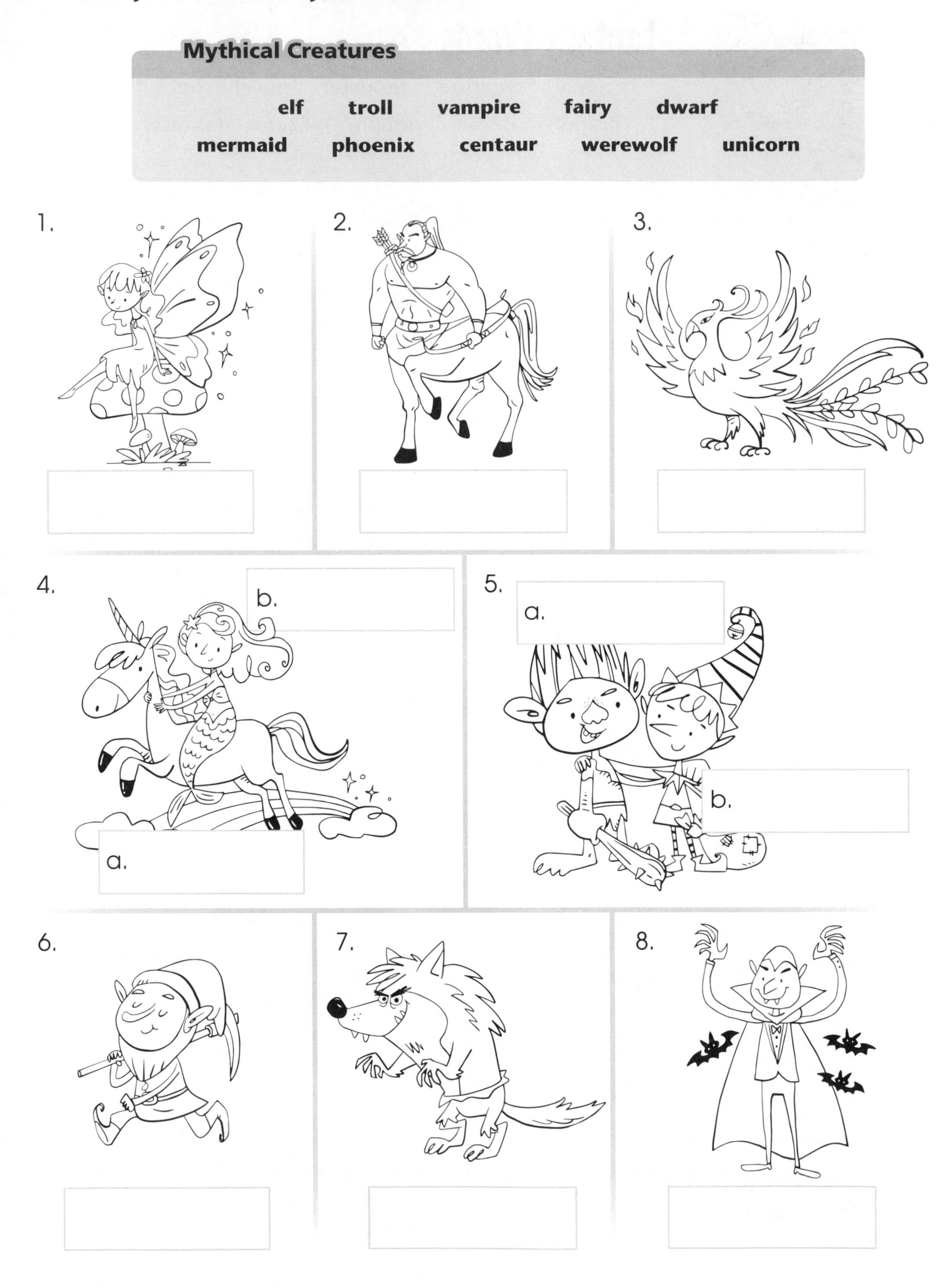

C. Read the clues and complete the crossword puzzle with fantasy words.

Across

- A magic words intended to bring harm or bad luck to someone
- B the study of changing metal to gold
- C a large, black pot witches use to brew potions
- D a witch
- E a small, human-like, old man guarding the earth's treasures

Down

1. a many-headed serpent
2. a form of words with magical power
3. a winged horse
4. a magical medicine

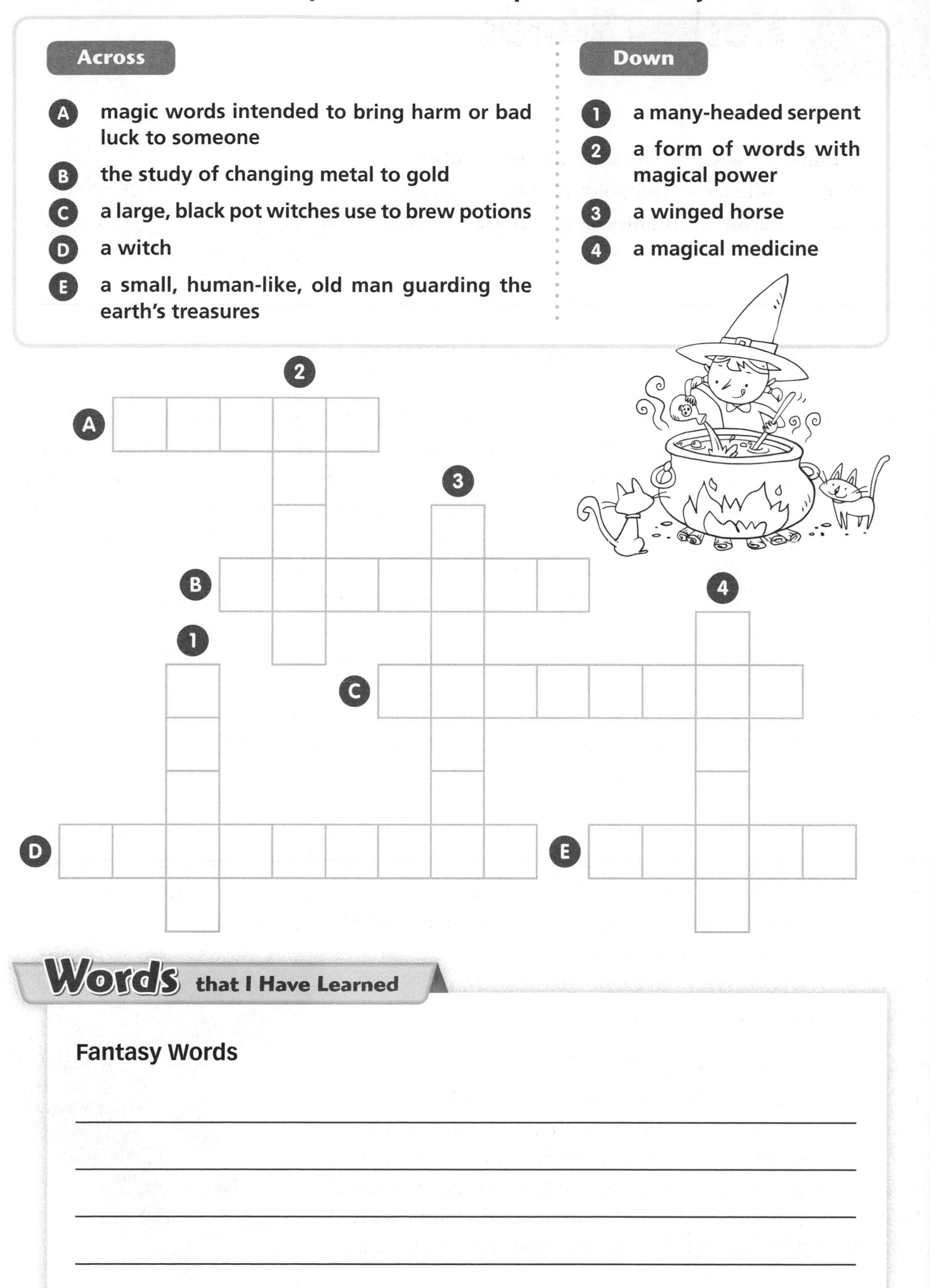

Words that I Have Learned

Fantasy Words

____

____

____

____

UNIT 5

Hockey Words

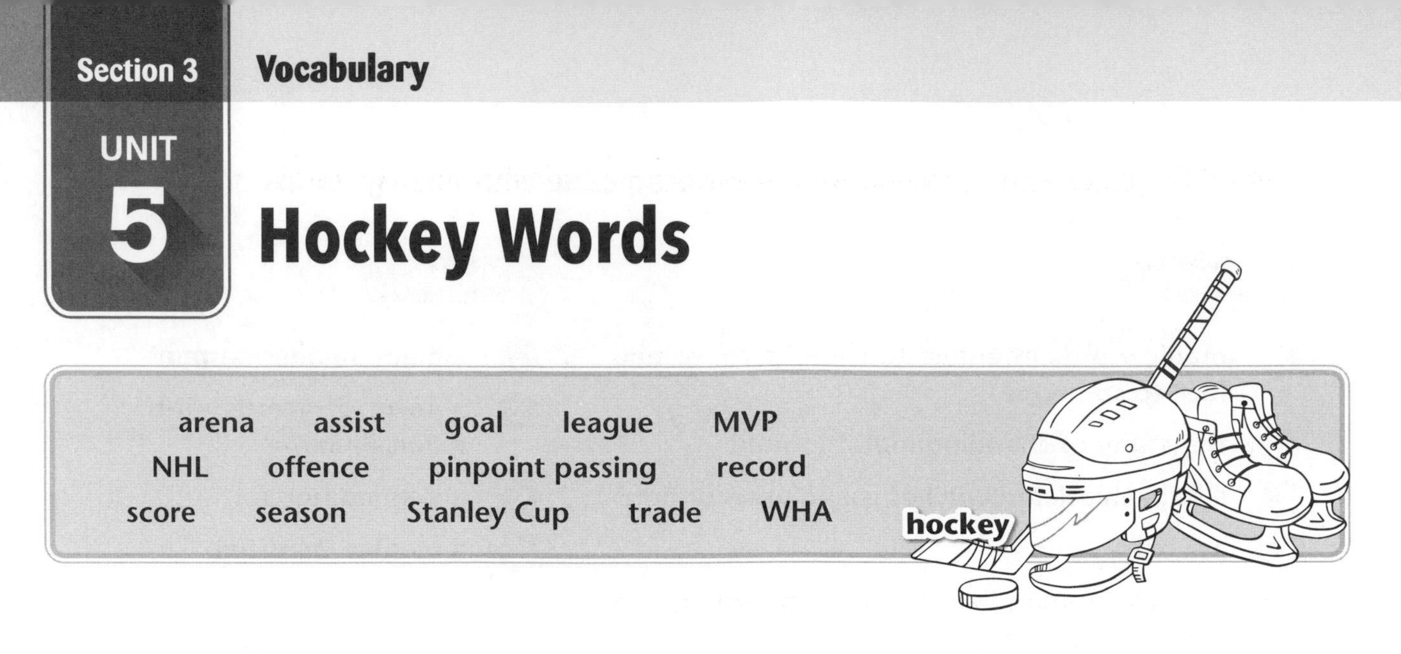

arena assist goal league MVP
NHL offence pinpoint passing record
score season Stanley Cup trade WHA

"The Great One" – Wayne Gretzky

At six years old, Wayne Gretzky played with the ten year olds in the Atom League in Brantford, Ontario. He made his professional debut in 1978 at the age of 18 with the Indianapolis Racers of the World Hockey Association (WHA). When the Racers fell into financial trouble, they sold Gretzky to the Edmonton Oilers. In his first season with the Oilers, Gretzky scored 43 goals and added 61 assists for a 72-game total of 104 points. When the WHA began to fall apart, the Edmonton Oilers were incorporated into the National Hockey League (NHL). In his first official year in the NHL, Gretzky amassed 51 goals and 86 assists for a total of 137 points. He was voted the league's most valuable player (MVP) – an honour he would go on to achieve eight consecutive times.

During his years with the Oilers, Gretzky broke Phil Esposito's scoring record with 92 goals, surpassing the 200-point per season milestone. Later, he established an all-time scoring record with 215 total points in a single season.

After the 1989 Stanley Cup victory, Gretzky was traded to the Los Angeles Kings, a team with a losing record and very few spectators. It did not take long, however, for people to come out to witness the Great One. In 1989, he broke Gordie Howe's lifetime scoring record of 1850 total points and went on to lead the Kings to the Stanley Cup finals. The once sparsely occupied arena in Los Angeles was then sold out for every home game.

Gretzky has the uncanny ability to control the offence of the game. Pinpoint passing, the knack for finding his teammates, and the creativity to mastermind scoring opportunities virtually every shift on the ice account for his total domination of hockey. When Gretzky retired in 1999, fans were saddened by the prospect that such a great player and ambassador for the game would never play again.

A. Read the meanings and write the correct hockey words. Then write the definitions for the given words.

Hockey Word		Meaning
1. ______________	:	the national sport of Canada played on ice
2. ______________	:	the National Hockey League
3. ______________	:	the best performance or score ever attained
4. ______________	:	the fixed time of the year when a particular sport is played
5. ______________	:	Most Valuable Player
6. ______________	:	a method or style of scoring attack
7. ______________	:	the World Hockey Association
8. ______________	:	a hockey championship trophy
9. ______________	:	a passing skill in hockey that requires acute accuracy
10. ______________	:	to exchange players among professional sports teams
11. ______________	:	a pass or an action of a player enabling a teammate to score a goal

12. arena: ______________________________

13. goal: ______________________________

14. league: ______________________________

15. score: ______________________________

Section 3

Vocabulary

B. Circle the correct hockey terms.

1. The champion was determined when Mike scored the **bar down / bar up** goal.

2. Joanne tried to score a goal but the puck **rebounded / shot** back into play.

3. **Squatting / Elbowing** is a penalty so players should not do it.

4. Punit is good at fooling his opponents by doing a lot of **dukes / dekes** .

5. The players waited while the **rink / field** got iced.

6. A hockey game starts off with a **shootout / faceoff** .

7. A **blueliner / bluestander** is a defenceman.

8. There are three **zones / areas** on a hockey rink: attacking, neutral, and defensive.

9. A **referee / coach** is responsible for supervising and enforcing the rules of a hockey game from a neutral point of view.

10. When a player scores three goals in succession in a game, it is called a **cap-trick / hat-trick** .

11. A **cupcake / muffin** is basically a weak shot.

12. A green **biscuit / cookie** is a hockey training puck.

13. Another name for a goalie in a hockey game is **netminder / netsaver** .

C. Label the diagram of a hockey player's uniform.

Hockey Uniform

helmet **shoulder pad** **hockey pants** **stick**
glove **elbow pad** **hockey sock** **skate**

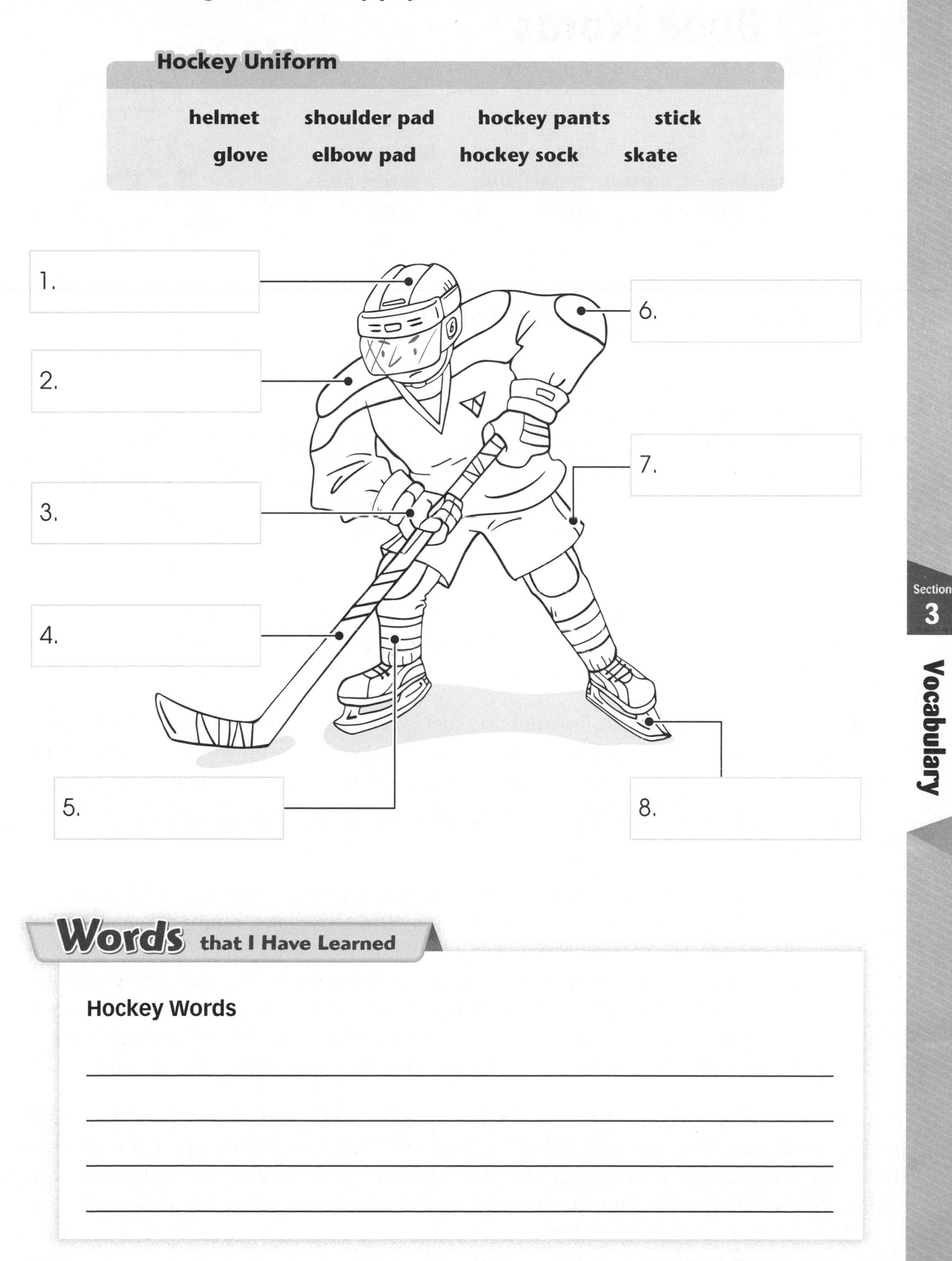

Words that I Have Learned

Hockey Words

Section 3 Vocabulary

UNIT 6 Book Words

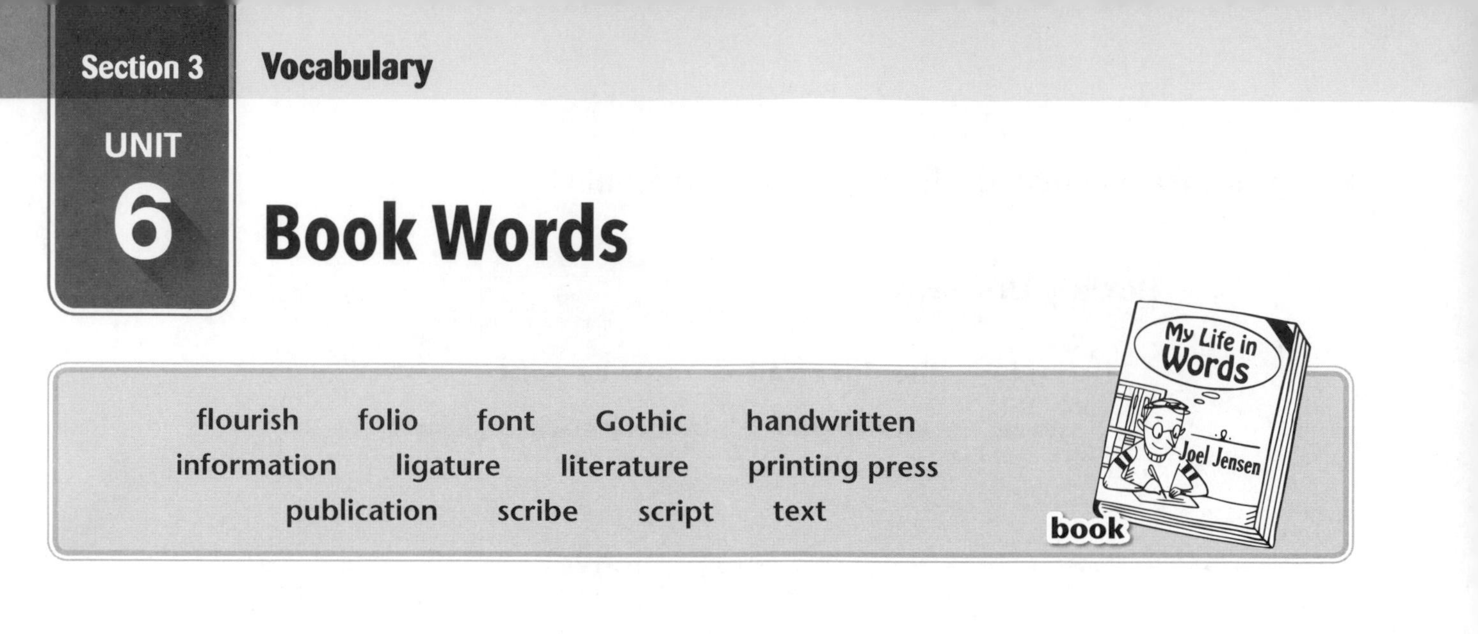

flourish folio font Gothic handwritten
information ligature literature printing press
publication scribe script text

The Pioneer of the Printing Press

Johannes Gutenberg was chosen to be the most important figure of the past millennium by the media. You may not be familiar with him but he has definitely influenced your life to some extent. Gutenberg is credited with inventing the printing press and consequently paving the way for printing books.

He was born into a noble family in the city of Mainz, Germany. His early training was in goldsmithing. In 1428, he moved to Strasbourg and lived there for over 20 years. It was in Strasbourg that he probably made his first experiments with movable type.

Gutenberg utilized techniques of metalwork, such as casting, punch cutting, and stamping for the mass production of books. In those days, books in Europe were handwritten by scribes in Gothic script with many flourishes and ligatures (interconnected letter pairs). To reproduce this "look", Gutenberg fashioned a font of over 300 characters, far larger than the fonts of today.

By 1450, Gutenberg was back in Mainz at work on a printing press. Between 1450 and 1455, while preparing to produce a large folio Latin Bible, Gutenberg is thought to have printed a number of smaller books, a calendar, and a papal Letter of Indulgence. The Bible of 42 Lines, the oldest surviving printed book in the Western world, was completed by August 15, 1456, and while it is now credited to Gutenberg, he appears to have been relieved of his supervisory position and his press before the time of its publication. Ironically, no printed material was ever credited to Gutenberg during his lifetime.

The discovery of the modern printing press changed the way information was delivered. In fact, this invention was responsible for educating the masses worldwide. Even today in the computer age, we rely heavily on the printed word of text for instruction, information, and for the pleasure of reading literature.

A. **Read the clues and write the book words on the lines.**

Clues

1. a set of characters of a certain style and size
2. produced and made available to the public
3. two or more letters joined together
4. facts or details about something
5. a decorative stroke in writing
6. a person who wrote books by hand
7. a book of the largest size
8. written or printed words
9. a body of written works
10. invented by Gutenberg
11. as opposed to "printed"
12. written characters
13. a font style

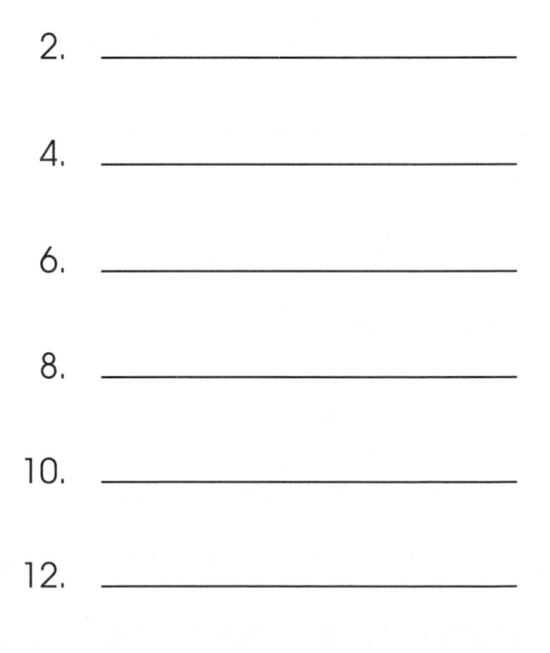

Book Words

1. ______________________ 2. ______________________

3. ______________________ 4. ______________________

5. ______________________ 6. ______________________

7. ______________________ 8. ______________________

9. ______________________ 10. ______________________

11. ______________________ 12. ______________________

13. ______________________

Section 3 Vocabulary

B. Fill in the blanks with the correct book words.

More Book Words

autobiography	table of contents	calligraphy	library	publishers	
author	journal	bookshop	epilogue	science fiction	synopsis

1. J. K. Rowling is the ________________ of the Harry Potter series.
2. The book's ________________ tells readers what happened to the characters after the story.
3. The famous activist wrote an ________________ of her own life because she has had an interesting life.
4. Penelope has to return the books to the ________________ so others can read them.
5. Arthur loves to write in his ________________ about his daily life.
6. The ________________ sells hundreds of books in different genres and on many different topics.
7. ________________ is Joel's favourite genre because he thinks it is exciting and futuristic.
8. Emily went to different ________________ in order to get her book published.
9. ________________ is the art of penmanship.
10. Carlton read the ________________ of the story on the back cover of the book and he thought it sounded interesting.
11. Donna took a look at the ________________ of the reference book to get an idea about the different topics covered.

C. Label the different parts of a book.

Parts of a Book

barcode title author pages synopsis
quote illustration spine publisher's logo

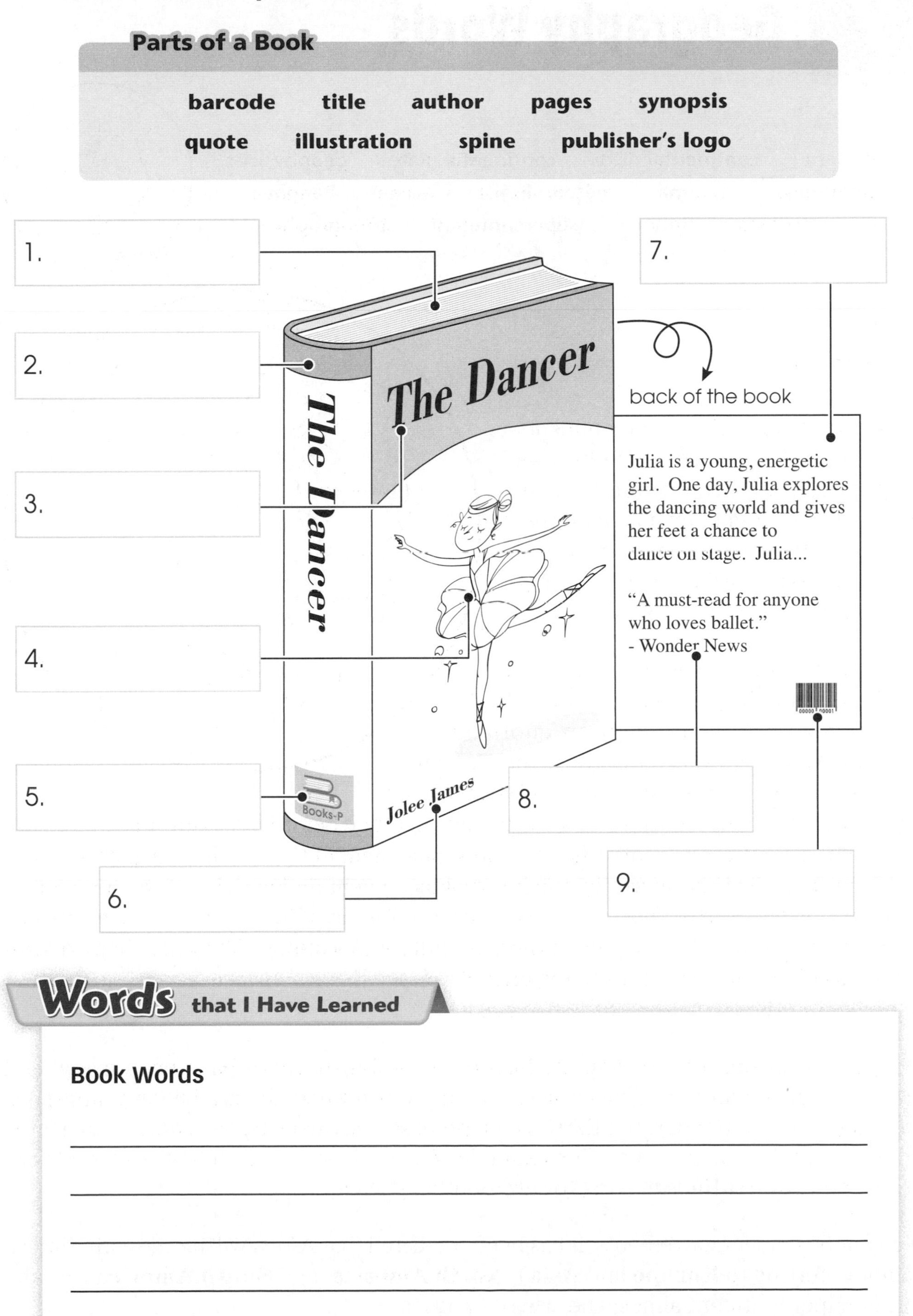

Words that I Have Learned

Book Words

UNIT 7

Geography Words

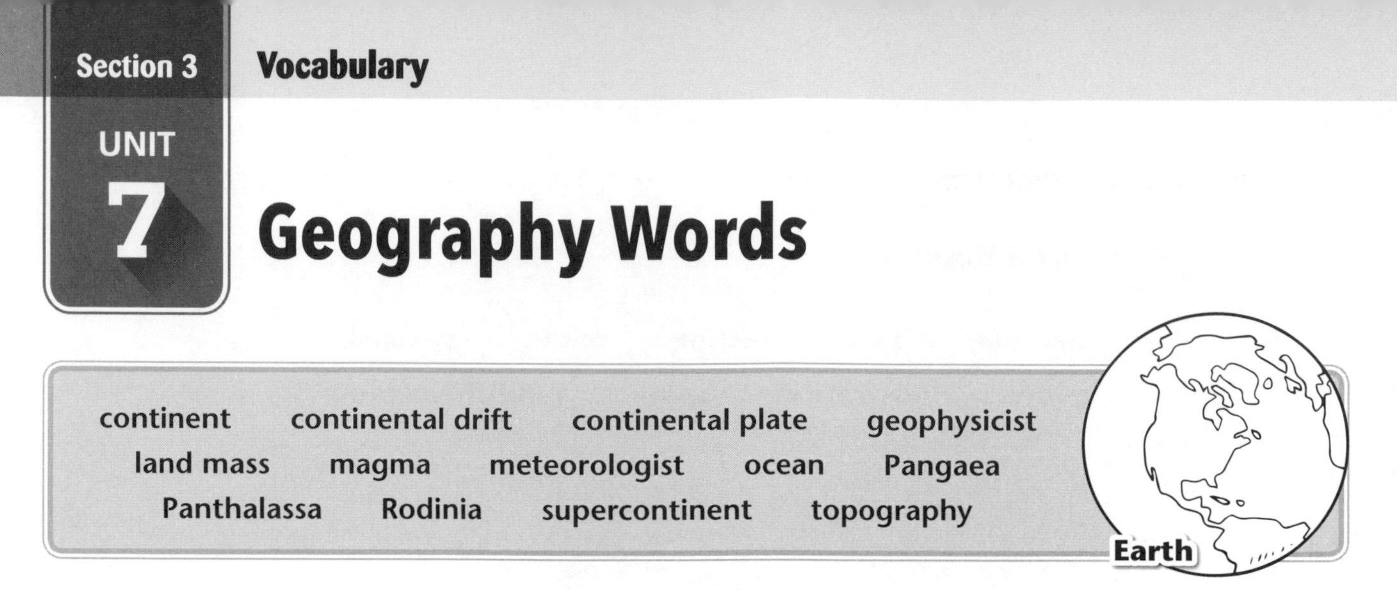

Pangaea

Millions of years ago, the seven continents that exist today were all joined as one gigantic supercontinent. This supercontinent was known as Pangaea. The word "Pangaea" comes from the Ancient Greek words "pan" meaning "all", and "gaia" meaning "land".

The supercontinent was located in the middle of one big global ocean called Panthalassa. The concept of an enormous piece of land was first introduced by the German meteorologist and geophysicist Alfred Wegener. He proposed that all the continents were joined together before breaking up due to the continental drift. Continental drift is the slow movement of the continental plates on the Earth's surface. This is caused by the internal movement and activity of the hot molten magma inside the Earth. These processes lead to the breaking apart of land masses as big as continents and the carrying of them to different locations. They also helped form the topography, which is the way a region looks on the Earth's surface, and were the main reason behind the formation of the five oceans.

It has also been said that during the history of the Earth, there have been many land masses similar to Pangaea. The earliest one that was formed about a billion years ago is called Rodinia. Even today, the Earth's own processes are causing the continental plates to move closer to each other. For example, **Africa** is slowly colliding with southern Europe, and **Australia** is moving toward Southeast Asia.

Based on the current movements, it has been predicted that Africa will merge with Eurasia (a name referring to **Europe** and **Asia**), **North America**, and **South America** to make another supercontinent almost the size of Pangaea.

A. **Unscramble the geography words. Then sort the words into the correct boxes. Write the letters.**

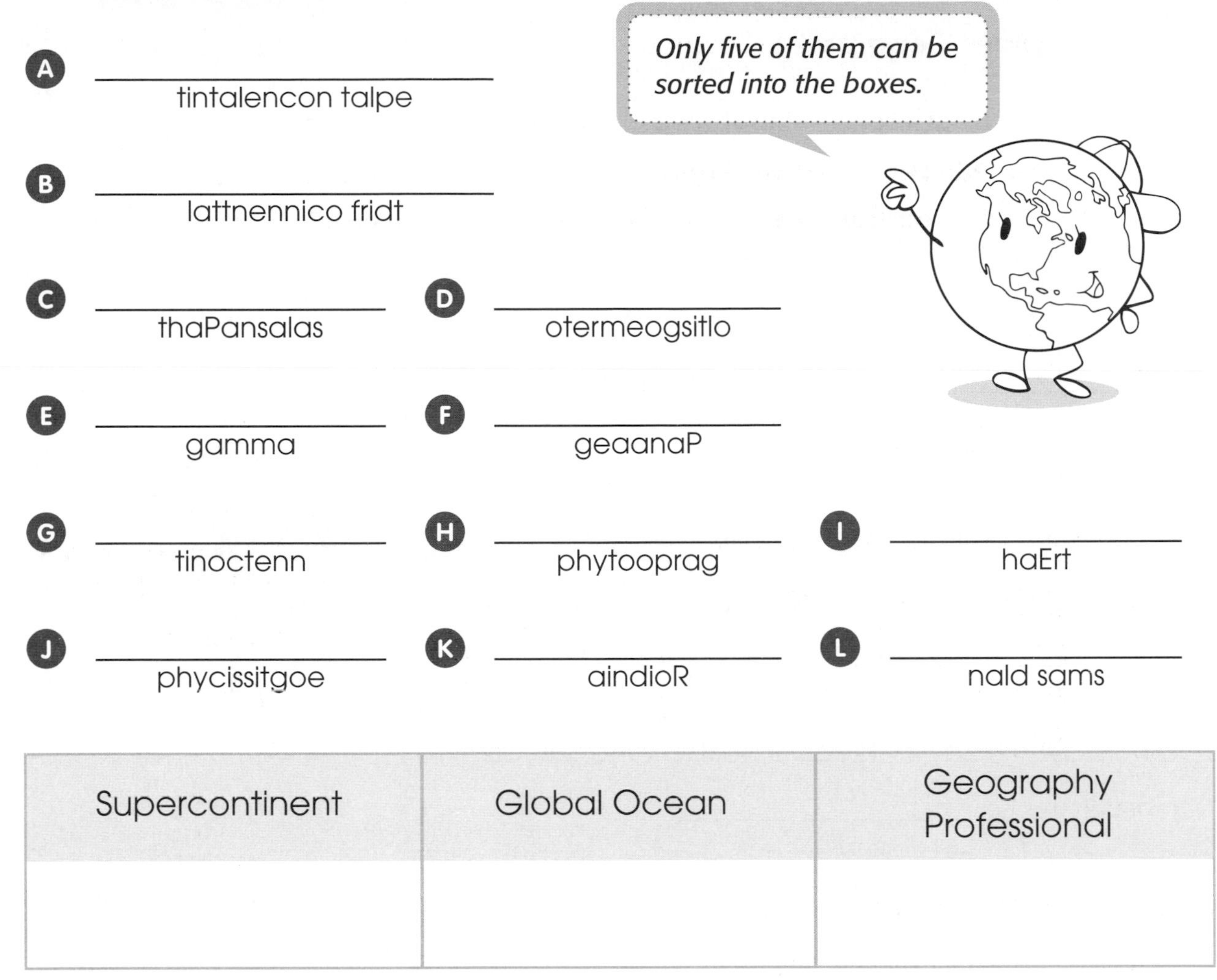

A ______________________ tintalencon talpe

B ______________________ lattnennico fridt

C ______________________ thaPansalas

D ______________________ otermeogsitlo

E ______________________ gamma

F ______________________ geaanaP

G ______________________ tinoctenn

H ______________________ phytooprag

I ______________________ haErt

J ______________________ phycissitgoe

K ______________________ aindioR

L ______________________ nald sams

Supercontinent	Global Ocean	Geography Professional

B. **Label the map with the geography words in bold from the passage.**

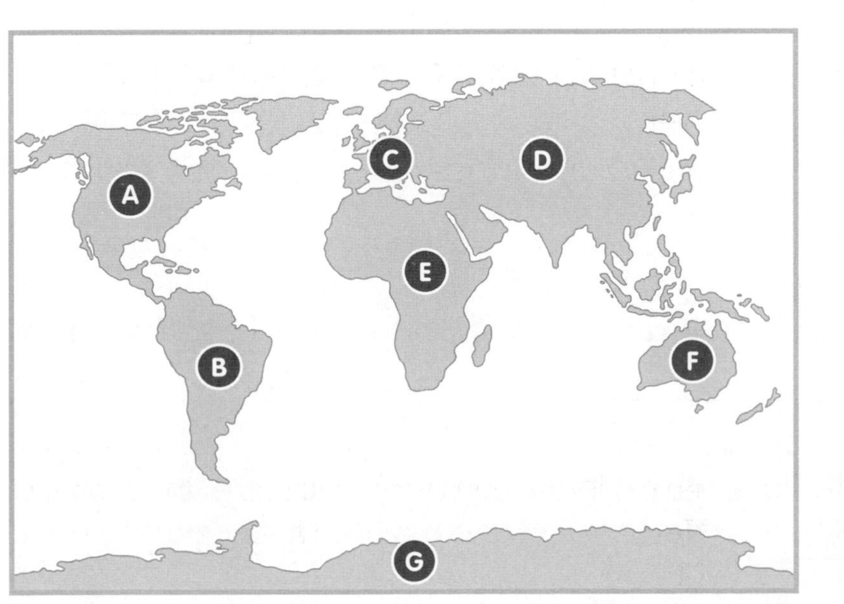

The Seven Continents

A ______________________

B ______________________

C ______________________

D ______________________

E ______________________

F ______________________

G Antarctica

C. **Fill in the blanks with the correct geography words.**

More Geography Words

equator landforms border meridian
North archipelago Arctic cartography
compass rose Global Positioning System

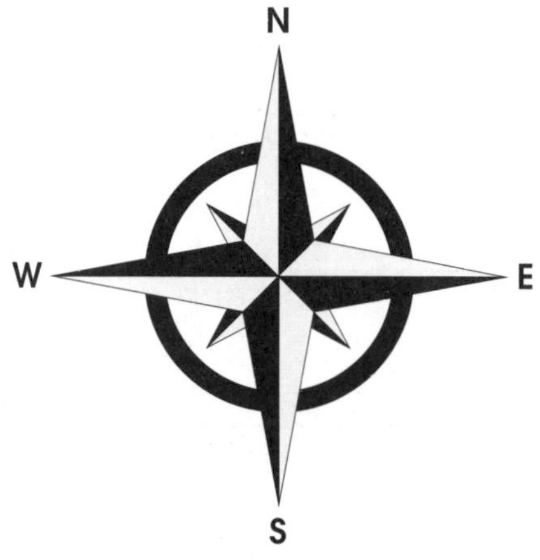

1. A ____________________ shows the cardinal directions on a map.

2. The imaginary line that divides the Earth into Northern and Southern Hemispheres is called the ____________________ .

3. Nowadays, many cars have built-in GPS, which stands for ____________________ .

4. There are many types of ____________________ including: hills, valleys, canyons, plains, and basins.

5. A ____________________ is a line separating two political or geographical regions, such as countries, provinces, and states.

6. ____________________ is the science or art of the production of maps.

7. An ____________________ is a group of islands or an area of sea that contains many islands.

8. The ____________________ is an imaginary line on the Earth's surface that passes through the ____________________ and South Poles.

9. The region near the North Pole, which includes the Arctic Ocean, is called the ____________________ .

D. **Identify and name the landforms.**

Landforms

canyon **plain** **mountain range**
island **butte** **plateau** **valley**

Words that I Have Learned

Geography Words

Section 3 Vocabulary

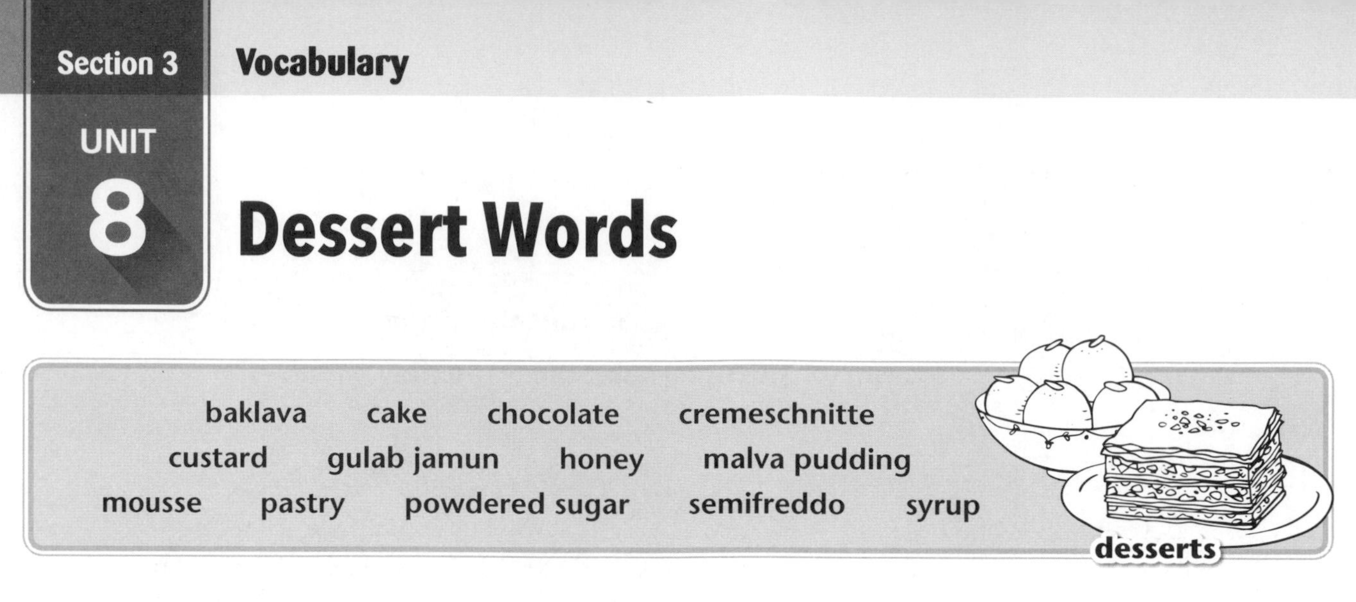

UNIT 8

Dessert Words

baklava cake chocolate cremeschnitte
custard gulab jamun honey malva pudding
mousse pastry powdered sugar semifreddo syrup

Desserts Galore

Joyce and Lori are at their favourite dessert restaurant, Desserts Galore.

"They have a new menu now," Joyce says. "Oh, look! There is a short description about each dessert."

"This one is called baklava," Lori reads. "It's a pastry that dates back to the Ottoman Empire! It has layers of filo and chopped nuts and is coated in honey."

"That sounds delicious. How about this one...semifreddo? They say it's like frozen chocolate mousse." Joyce looks at Lori in delight.

"Oh, this one sounds good too. It's called gulab jamun. It's a round Indian sweet made of milk solids dunked in syrup. The menu says that it is typically eaten during festivities," beams Lori.

"I don't know what milk solids are," Joyce replies. "But I like anything with syrup!"

"Yes, it looks really soft and yummy."

"But I think I've found my winner! Cremeschnitte. It's a Croatian custard cream cake dusted with powdered sugar and I am ordering it!" Joyce puts down her menu and signals to the waiter that she is ready to order.

"I will have the cremeschnitte, please!" Joyce orders decidedly.

"Good choice, miss, but my personal favourite is the malva pudding from South Africa. It is best with a cream sauce poured over it," the waiter says with two thumbs up.

Joyce stops smiling and heaves a heavy sigh. She says, "May I see the menu again, please? I don't think I saw that one."

Chuckling, the waiter returns the menu to Joyce. "I understand. Choosing the perfect dessert is an important decision," he says. The waiter gives the two girls a friendly wink and leaves them pondering their desserts.

A. Fill in the blanks with the correct dessert words to complete the sentences.

MENU

dessert
powdered sugar
pudding **honey**
pastry **cake**
custard **mousse**
chocolate **syrup**

1. ________________ is Valeria's favourite part of dinner.
2. Sean poured a lot of ________________ on his breakfast waffles.
3. My mom cannot drink tea without a drop of ________________ .
4. The black forest ________________ is topped with cherries.
5. Crème brûlée is a rich, creamy ________________ with a crispy layer of caramelized sugar on top.
6. Uncle Dominic is a ________________ chef at a famous dessert restaurant. His maple pecan Danish is my favourite.
7. The ice cream parlour offers a wide variety of both traditional and new flavours, but Aria always picks the ________________ flavour.
8. ________________ is a dessert that is usually dairy-based and thickened with gelatin or corn starch.
9. The light and fluffy ________________ is made with whipped cream and beaten egg whites.
10. My little brother likes licking the ________________ off his cremeschnitte before he eats the rest.

B. Label the desserts. Then draw and name your favourite dessert in the box. Write a short description of it.

C. **Match the dessert words with the pictures.**

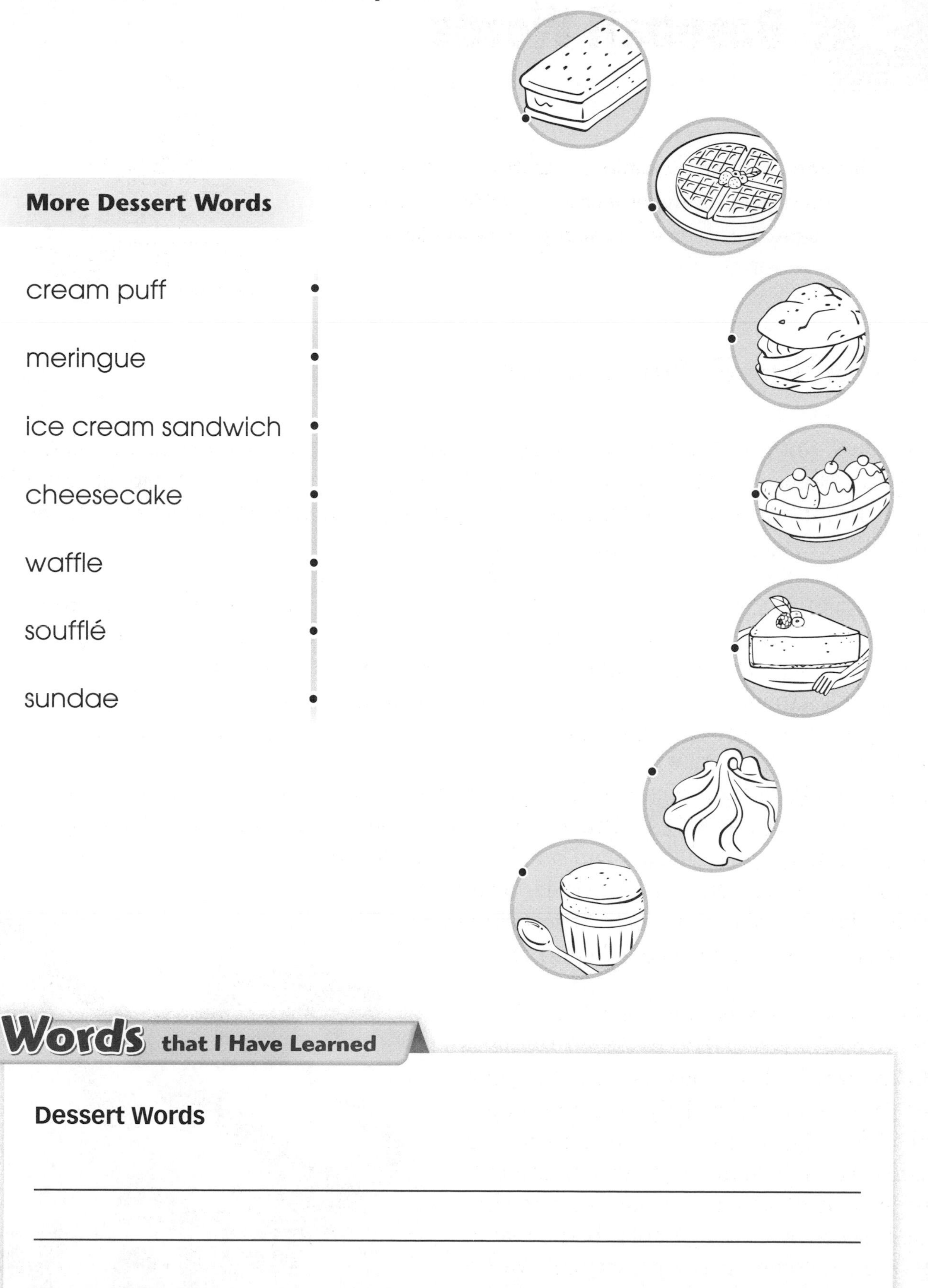

Words that I Have Learned

Dessert Words

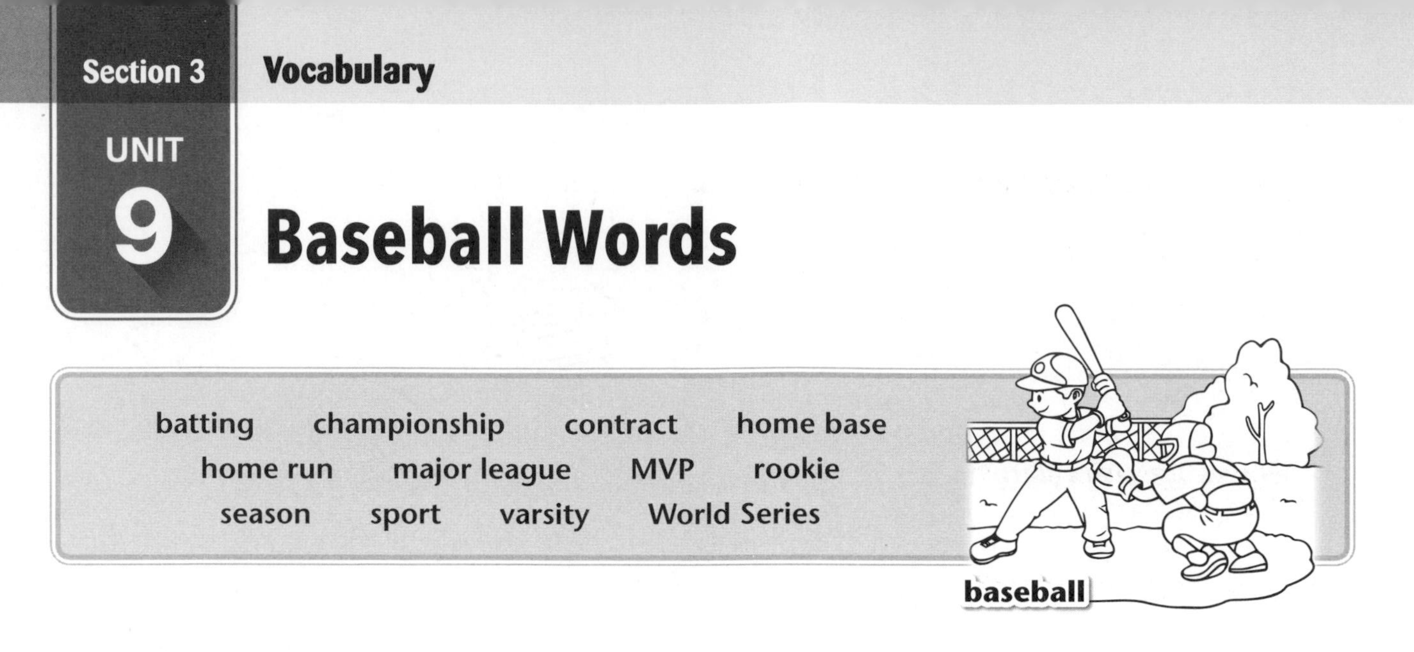

UNIT 9

Baseball Words

batting championship contract home base
home run major league MVP rookie
season sport varsity World Series

The Jackie Robinson Story

When Jack Roosevelt Robinson (Jackie Robinson) trotted onto Ebbets Field, home of the Brooklyn Dodgers baseball team, on April 15, 1947, he became the first African-American to play major league baseball, and the first brave step in breaking the colour barrier against black players was boldly taken.

Jackie was born on January 31, 1913 in Cairo, Georgia. He attended Pasadena Junior College where he led the Pasadena varsity baseball team to the championship and was voted MVP (Most Valuable Player). After graduation, Jackie was offered numerous scholarships to major universities. He chose UCLA and when he joined the Kansas City Monarchs of the Negro League, he was finally being paid to do what he did best.

Professional baseball was a segregated sport. Black players were prohibited from playing. On August 28, 1945, Branch Rickey, a forward-thinking Dodgers manager, signed Jackie Robinson to a contract and sent him to play for the Montreal Royals. On April 10, 1947, history was made. Jackie became the first African-American to sign a major league baseball contract.

When Jackie stepped onto New York's Ebbets Field that opening day, he faced the jeers of the crowd. The Dodgers won the game 5-3 and Jackie scored the winning home run. Over the next few seasons, he was to endure racial insults, prejudicial treatment, and even death threats. Jackie answered the public scorn by winning Rookie of the Year in 1947 and helping the Dodgers win the World Series in 1955. He helped the Dodgers win six pennants in ten years and stole home base an unprecedented 19 times.

Jackie Robinson retired in 1956 with a lifetime batting average of 0.311. In 1962, he was inducted into the National League Hall of Fame – the first African-American player to receive the honour. He is remembered as a courageous man who single-handedly broke the colour barrier in professional baseball. Robinson died in 1972. His epitaph reads: "A life is not important except in the impact it has on other lives".

A. Unscramble the baseball words and fill in the blanks.

1. Baseball is one of the most watched ______________ (tspros) in Canada.
2. The new player read his ______________ (tarccont) carefully before signing it.
3. Monica was voted ______________ (PMV) of her school's women's baseball team.
4. Adrian wants to play in the ______________ (rajom elegau) one day.
5. Oliver's team won the ______________ (ampshipchion) three times in a row.
6. By proving his ______________ (atigbtn) abilities, Brian convinced the manager of his favourite team to sign him up.
7. Our university established its first ______________ (yiavrst) baseball team in 1981.
8. Everyone thinks the ______________ (okorei) will one day be the star player.
9. Do you know which baseball team has won the most games in a ______________ (sonesa)?
10. Maria touched ______________ (oehm sabe) just in time.
11. Tom dreams of attending the ______________ (olrWd ereisS) with his best friend.
12. It was the captain who hit a ______________ (meoh nru) and won the game.

Section 3 Vocabulary

B. Check the correct baseball words for the definitions.

Let's learn baseball lingo!

1. consists of two halves; in each half one team bats until there are three outs each
   - ○ inning
   - ○ lineup

2. the next batter to bat following the current batter
   - ○ on-deck
   - ○ hit the dirt

3. where players sit in the dugout
   - ○ belt
   - ○ bench

4. when a team has zero on the scoreboard
   - ○ goose egg
   - ○ granny

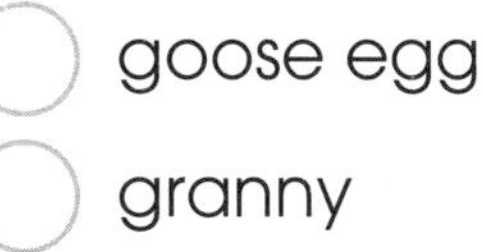

5. a pitcher's best pitch
   - ○ money pitch
   - ○ money ball

6. a pitch that curves
   - ○ curveball
   - ○ bleeder

7. when there is a player on base
   - ○ aboard
   - ○ assist

8. a fastball
   - ○ chuck
   - ○ cheese

9. to hit a ball very hard
   - ○ handle
   - ○ hammer

10. a left-handed pitcher
    - ○ southpaw
    - ○ northpaw

11. a batter who hits many home runs and extra base hits
    - ○ power stroke
    - ○ power hitter

C. **Label the baseball field with the correct positions of baseball players.**

Positions

- Pitcher
- Catcher
- First Base
- Second Base
- Third Base
- Short Stop
- Left Field
- Right Field
- Centre Field

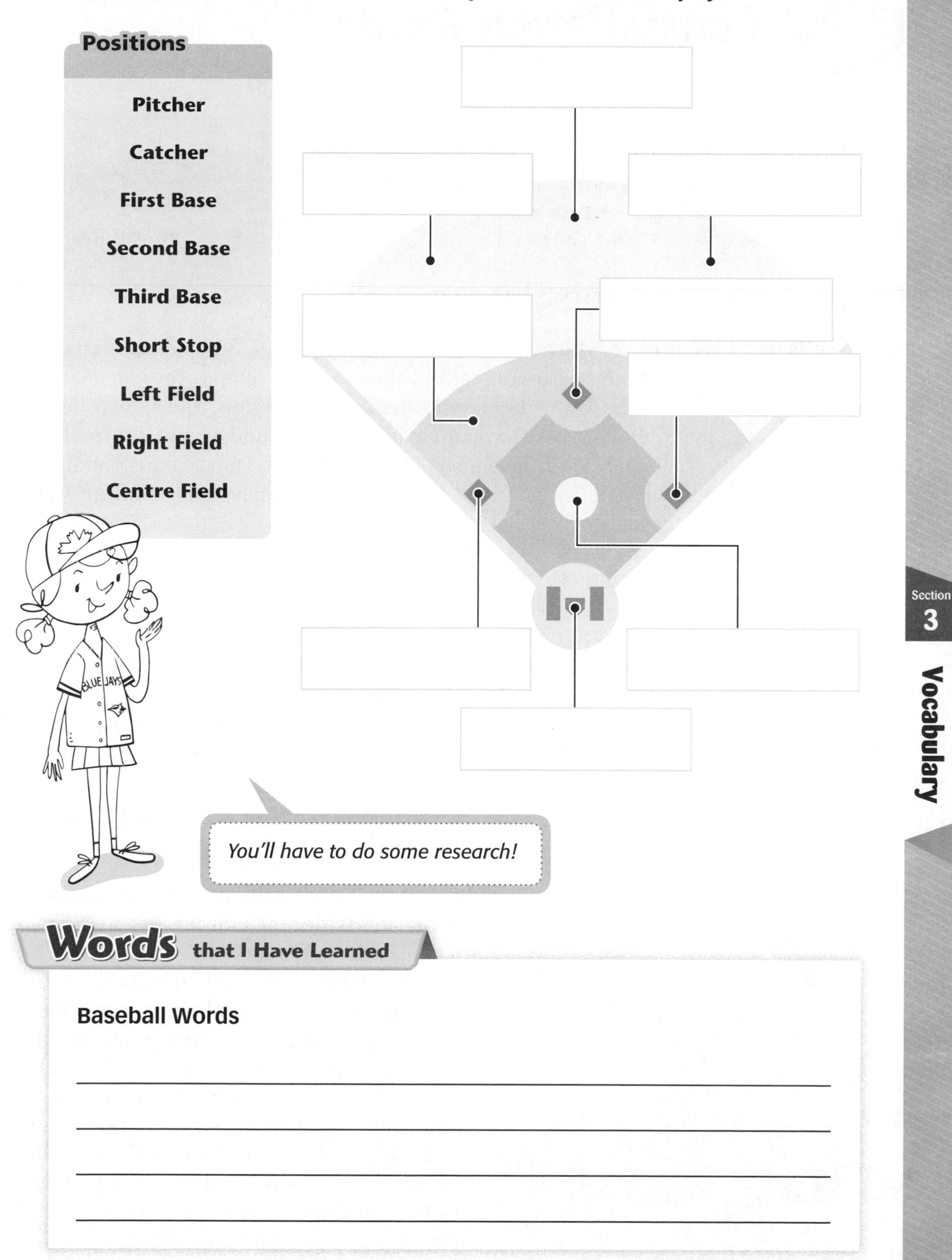

Words that I Have Learned

Baseball Words

____

____

____

____

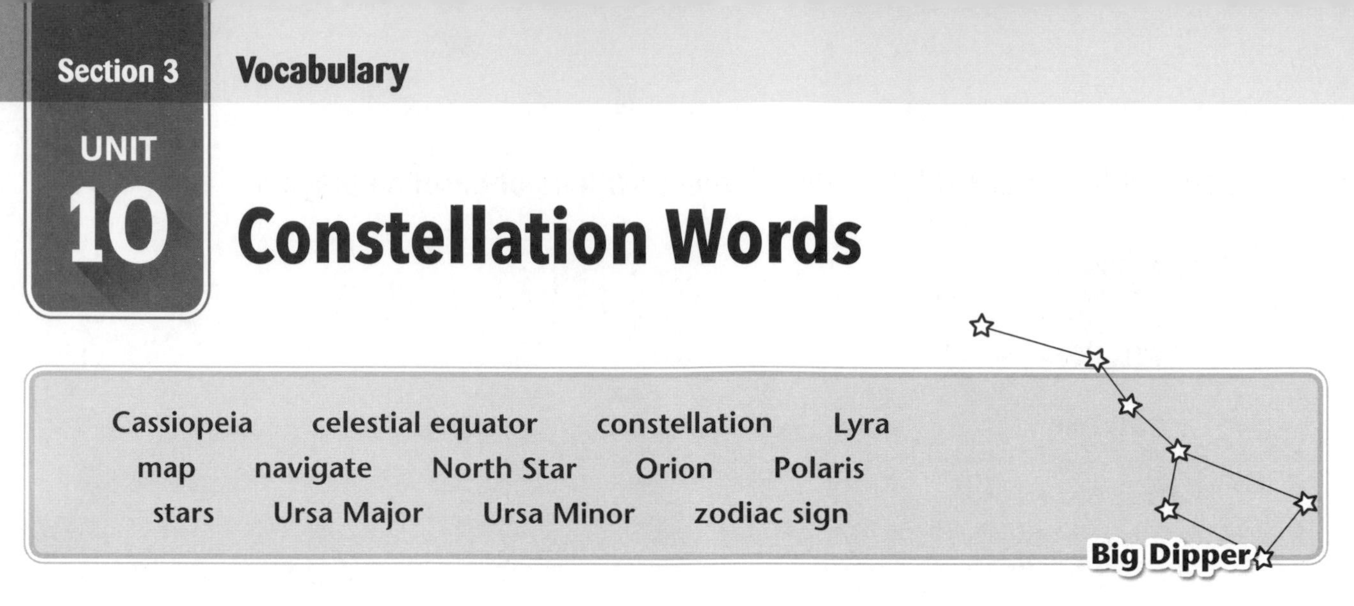

UNIT 10 Constellation Words

Cassiopeia celestial equator constellation Lyra
map navigate North Star Orion Polaris
stars Ursa Major Ursa Minor zodiac sign

Constellations in the Sky

A **constellation** is a pattern of **stars** in the sky that forms an image. Constellations usually represent mythological characters, creatures, and objects. For example, the constellation **Cassiopeia** symbolizes the vain queen who insulted Poseidon; the constellation **Ursa Major** is the nymph Callisto, with whom Zeus was in love and who was turned into a bear by Hera out of jealousy; and the constellation **Lyra** is the musical instrument of the musician Orpheus, whose music enchanted both human and beast. The **zodiac signs** are also constellations in the sky.

Constellations had different purposes in ancient times. They were a way for people to keep track of time. People observed the placement of the constellations in the sky as the Earth orbited **the sun** and knew when to plant or harvest their crops, or when the season was going to change. Constellations were also used as a map. Before the compass was invented, sea voyagers used the stars to **navigate** their way. Explorers looked to Polaris (**the North Star**), which belongs to the constellation **Ursa Minor**, to guide their way. To find Polaris, simply locate **the Big Dipper**, which consists of seven stars of the constellation Ursa Major, first. Then draw an imaginary line from the two stars at the outer edge of the Big Dipper toward Ursa Minor and you will find Polaris.

One of the most famous constellations is **Orion**. It is one of the largest and most recognizable **celestial** objects, and can be seen throughout the year anywhere in the world. Located on the **celestial equator**, it is named after the Greek hunter, Orion, who was hunting with the goddess Artemis one day and declared that he would kill all the animals in the world. Angered, Gaea, the goddess of the Earth, sent a scorpion to kill him. The grief-stricken Artemis asked Zeus to place Orion in the heavens – which Zeus did, along with the scorpion that killed Orion.

A. Fill in the blanks with the constellation words in bold in the passage.

1. the luminous sphere in the sky held by its own gravity ____________________

2. the constellation representing the nymph Callisto ____________________

3. used to locate the North Star ____________________

4. the North Star belongs to this constellation ____________________

5. to move or direct in a plotted course ____________________

6. also called Polaris ____________________

7. the constellation named after a Greek hunter ____________________

8. used to find one's way when lost ____________________

9. the constellation representing the musical instrument of the musician Orpheus ____________________

10. the great circle of the celestial sphere; lies on the same plane as Earth's equator ____________________

11. Taurus, Leo, Virgo, Sagittarius, Aquarius, etc. ____________________

12. the constellation symbolizing the vain queen who insulted Poseidon ____________________

13. a group of stars forming an image and is named ____________________

14. of or relating to the sky ____________________

B. Research the constellations and then draw them.

Lyra

Ursa Major

Ursa Minor

Orion

C. **Identify and name the zodiac signs.**

- **Aquarius**
  (the Water-bearer)
- **Aries**
  (the Ram)
- **Cancer**
  (the Crab)
- **Capricorn**
  (the Sea-goat)
- **Gemini**
  (the Twins)
- **Leo**
  (the Lion)
- **Libra**
  (the Balance)
- **Pisces**
  (the Fishes)
- **Sagittarius**
  (the Archer)
- **Scorpio**
  (the Scorpion)
- **Taurus**
  (the Bull)
- **Virgo**
  (the Virgin)

Words that I Have Learned

Constellation Words

____

____

____

____

UNIT 11

Charity Words

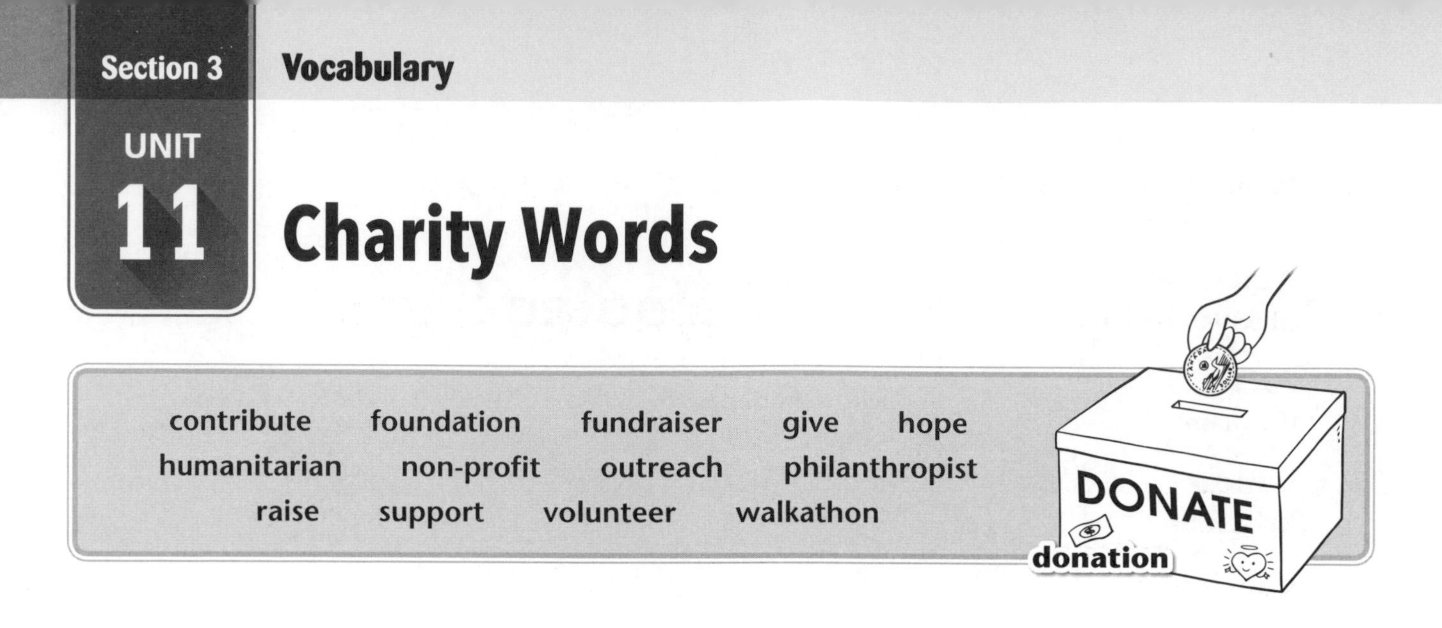

contribute foundation fundraiser give hope
humanitarian non-profit outreach philanthropist
raise support volunteer walkathon

Charity – What Is It?

All across the globe, philanthropists, non-profit organizations, and charitable foundations that want to make a change inspire hope by giving back to the world. Their humanitarian efforts have helped millions of people, such as those displaced by natural disasters and war and those born into poverty. Community outreach programs, which include non-profit groups, identify specific needs within the community and provide services for those who require them.

But how can you contribute?

It is hard to know where to start, but even a small donation to a worthy cause can affect change for the better. You can go online and research lists of charitable foundations, organizations, and causes that speak to you. You can even donate to creditable causes online, a simple and effective way to make a difference!

But if you do not have the means to donate, you can contribute your time and volunteer at your local soup kitchens, food drives, and fundraisers instead. You can participate in charity-driven walkathons, help organize a food or toy drive or charity talent show at your school, or simply offer a kind gesture of support to those in need.

One of the most important ways to contribute is to raise awareness. Be sure to share articles on social media about issues that are important to you. You can also research about humanitarian causes and share that information with your friends and family. And always remember to ask questions about how you can help!

A. Write the letters to match the charity words with their meanings.

Charity Word	Meaning
◯ humanitarian	**A** a person or event involved in collecting financial support for a charitable organization or cause
◯ non-profit	**B** an effort to bring services and information to people where they live
◯ fundraiser	**C** a person who seeks to help those in need, especially through financial support
◯ foundation	**D** non-business oriented; dedicated to supporting a cause without financial gain
◯ outreach	**E** concerned with or involved in promoting human welfare and reducing hardship
◯ philanthropist	**F** an organization that provides financial aid for a particular need

B. Complete the diagram with the correct charity words.

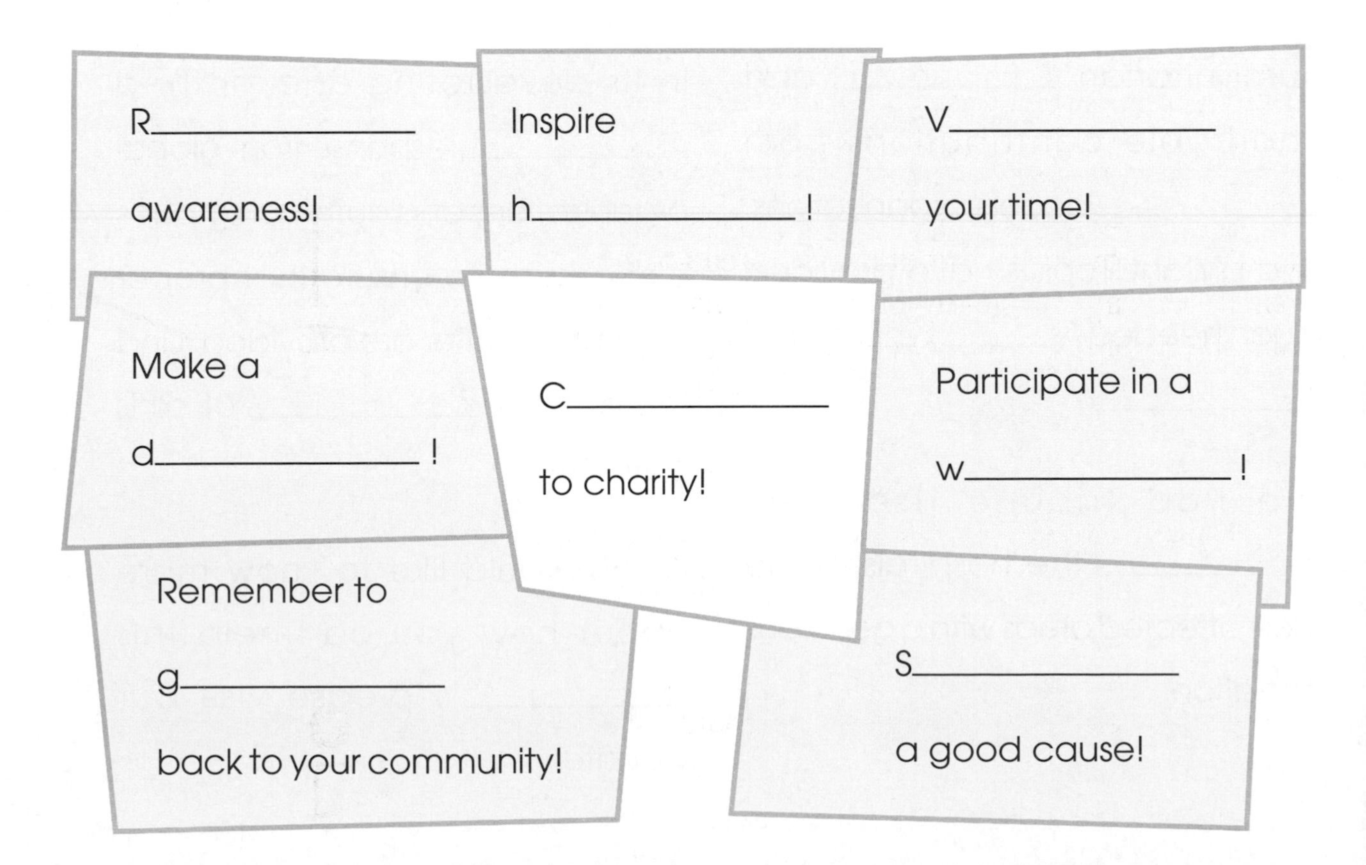

Section 3 Vocabulary

C. Fill in the blanks with the correct charity words to complete the news article.

More Charity Words

humane **benevolent** **cause** **endow**
aid **needy** **relief** **welfare**

The Pop Tribune

September 20, 2019

Hurricane Relief Efforts Underway

By Zinda Lane

Hurricane Thomas, a massive storm that hit our coastline this past week, has drawn the attention of the world.

Humanitarian 1. ____________ and charitable contributions from 2. ____________ leaders, organizations, and philanthropists have provided much needed 3. ____________ for the 4. ____________ .

The Pop Tribune itself will 5. ____________ the hospitals of the most affected areas with a generous donation.

In its devastating aftermath, a 6. ____________ response from global organizations and outreach groups is necessary to ensure that proper food and shelter are provided, and the general 7. ____________ of all is protected.

If you would like to know more about how you can help this 8. ____________ , please visit our website.

D. Circle the correct words to complete the sentences.

1. Remember to volunteer your time to a good **cause / commodity** if you do not have the monetary means to do so.

2. A **malevolent / benevolent** response to other people's suffering shows that you are a compassionate person.

3. The **adversity / welfare** of all people is a goal we should strive toward.

4. There are many **humane / self-serving** causes that you can contribute to.

E. Complete the sentences using the given charity words.

1. aid

   It is important to provide ____________________

   ____

2. relief

   After major disasters ____________________

   ____

3. endow

   Philanthropists and charitable organizations often ____________________

   ____

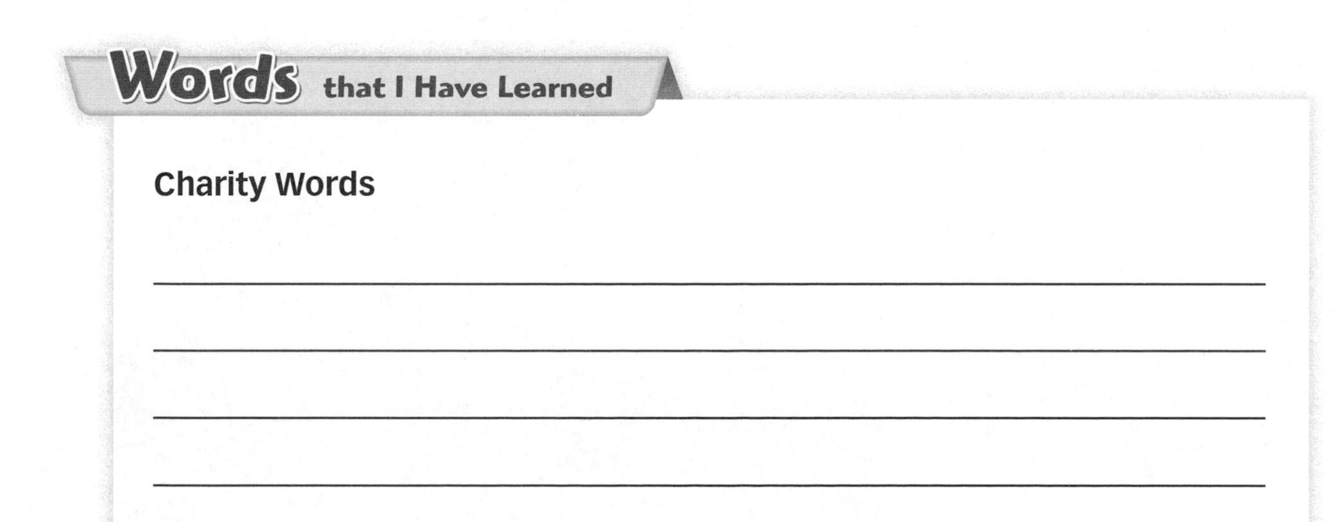

Section 3 Vocabulary

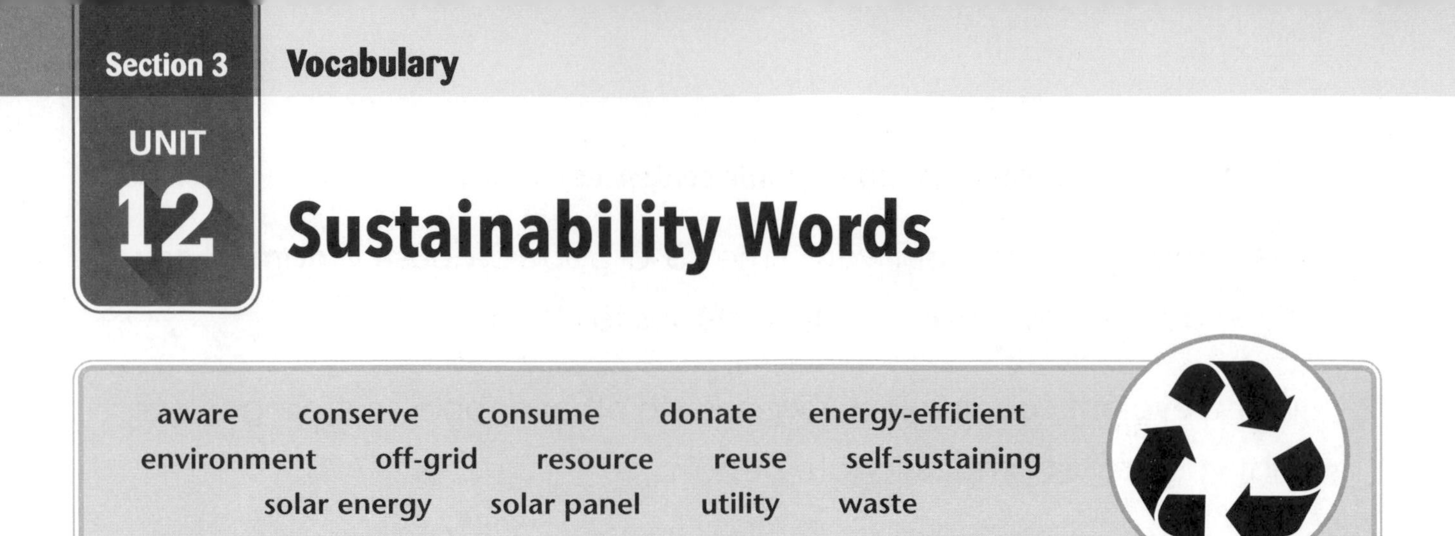

UNIT 12

Sustainability Words

aware conserve consume donate energy-efficient
environment off-grid resource reuse self-sustaining
solar energy solar panel utility waste

recycle

Living Sustainably

Living sustainably means using resources wisely and being aware of the amount of utilities such as gas, water, and electricity that you consume. It also means making efforts to produce less waste and taking care of the environment around you. Some of the ways you and your family can live sustainably at home include opening the windows instead of turning on the air conditioning, hanging your clothes to dry instead of using the dryer, using energy-efficient appliances, and recycling, reusing, and donating unused items.

Also, you and your family could try growing your own food! Installing solar panels to make use of the sun's energy to provide basic utilities or cooking food on wood burning stoves are also some methods of conserving resources. You might have to make some changes in your current lifestyle but living sustainably can be fun! Most importantly, it is environmentally friendly and definitely less expensive than the way most of us live today!

Due to these and many other factors, some people have even chosen to live "off-grid". Living off-grid means living in a self-sustaining manner. Houses that are built off the grid do not rely on the government's electric or water supply. Some people build small houses that are easy to maintain with little use of resources. They use rain catchers or wells for water, farm their own crops, and even keep animals to provide eggs, milk, and meat.

It might seem like a big change or hard work to live sustainably but it is achievable if you take it one step at a time. You do not have to live completely off-grid in order to live sustainably!

A. **Match the sustainability words with the correct definitions. Write the letters on the lines.**

A recycle
B solar panel
C solar energy
D waste
E utility
F aware
G self-sustaining
H resource
I conserve
J environment
K off-grid
L consume

1. ______ having knowledge or perception of something
2. ______ absorbs energy from the sun to produce electricity or heat
3. ______ examples include gas, water, and electricity
4. ______ one's surroundings and all that they consist of including living and non-living things
5. ______ to collect and treat used materials so that they can be reused
6. ______ being able to sustain one's self
7. ______ living in a manner that is not reliant on the government's water or electric supply
8. ______ energy from the sun that can be converted into solar power
9. ______ discarded and/or useless material
10. ______ to use; to devour; to absorb; to spend
11. ______ a source of supplies from which one benefits
12. ______ to avoid wasteful use of

B. Circle the correct sustainability words to complete the sentences.

1. We must all turn to **renewable / non-renewable** energy because it is more efficient and will never run out.

2. **Soil / Wind** is a non-polluting type of renewable energy that does not use fossil fuels or produce greenhouse gases or toxic waste.

3. **Donating / Dumping** used clothes is one way to reduce clothing waste and keep them out of landfills.

4. Carbon **footprint / handprint** is the amount of greenhouse gases produced to support human activities.

5. Reducing our carbon footprint will help **boost / ease** global warming and create a sustainable environment for our future generations.

6. An **ecohouse / envirohome** is a house that has low impact on the environment.

7. One way to live "green" is to stop using plastic and other materials that are not **biodegradable / consumable** .

8. We can **buy / reuse** cardboard boxes as storage containers.

9. Living sustainably is an important **commitment / burden** we have to nature.

C. Label the diagram with the sustainability words.

Sustainability Words

donate clothes **conserve water** **compost**
LED bulbs **energy-efficient appliances**

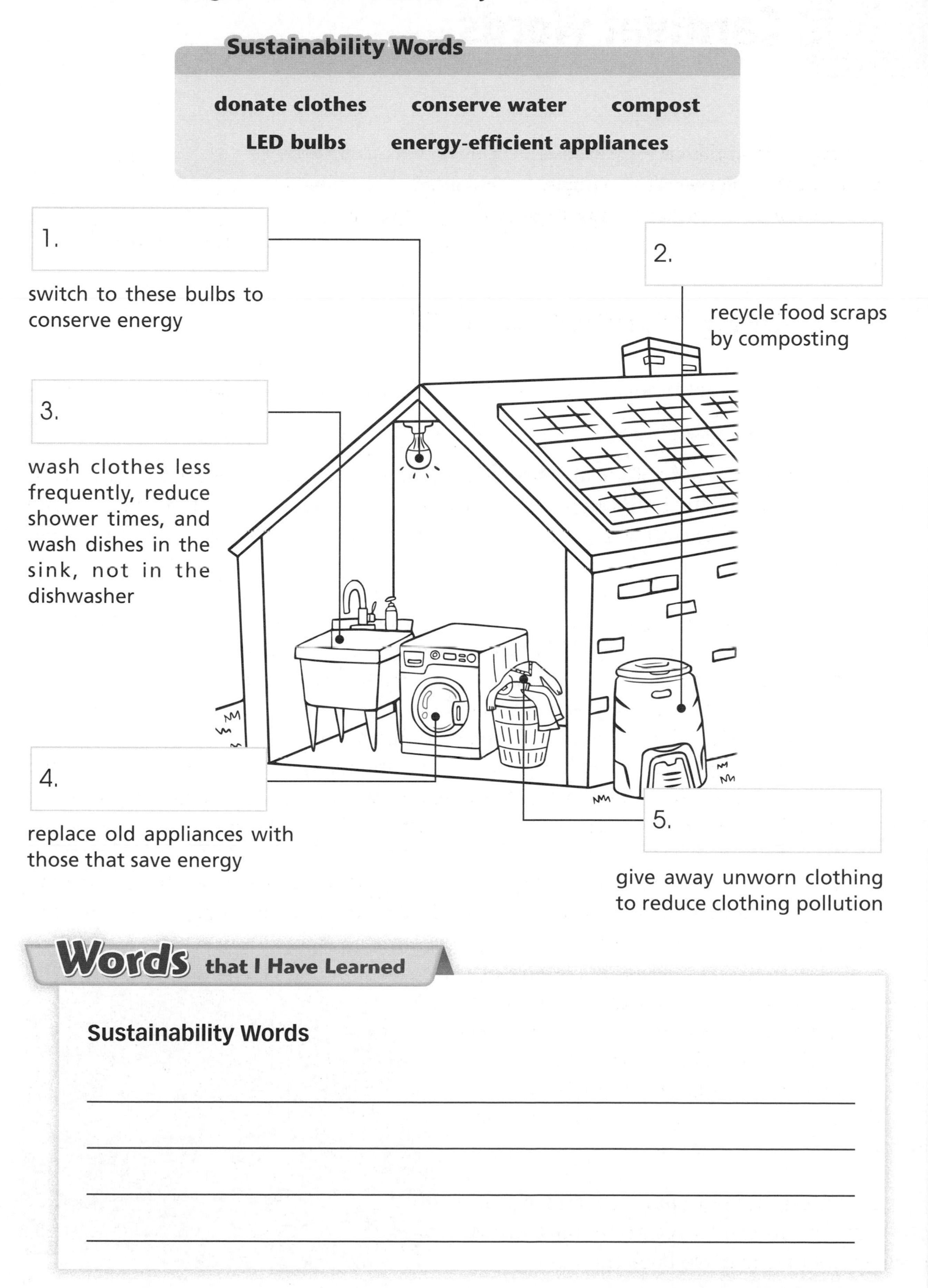

Words that I Have Learned

Sustainability Words

____

____

____

____

UNIT 13

Carnival Words

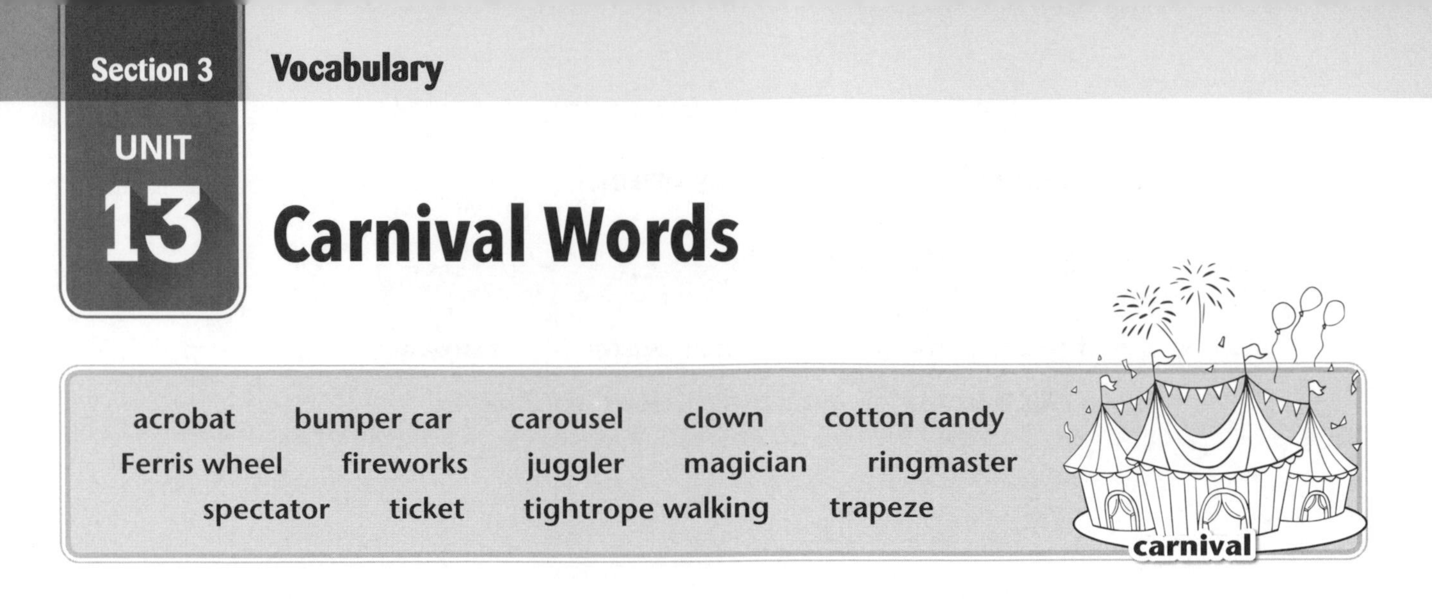

acrobat bumper car carousel clown cotton candy
Ferris wheel fireworks juggler magician ringmaster
spectator ticket tightrope walking trapeze

The Travelling Summer Carnival

One of my favourite memories is going to the Travelling Summer Carnival with my cousins back in 2015.

My mother drove my aunt, Eshaal, Anorah, and me to a big green field decorated with colourful banners, tents, and a huge Ferris wheel at one end. We quickly bought some cotton candies, paid for our tickets, and giggled as we took our seats right by the ring in the centre of the tent.

After a while, the show began with the simple announcement "Ladies and gentlemen, boys and girls...Let the show begin!" With this, a group of acrobats dressed in sparkly red and white costumes walked out, bowed, and took their positions as bright lights shone on their faces. I gasped as they accomplished one feat after another! They swung on trapezes, performed acrobatic feats, and took on tightrope walking. This was followed by jugglers gracefully juggling multiple objects at once and magicians wowing us by making balloons appear out of their black hats. At the end of the show, the ringmaster came out and thanked the spectators as we greeted him with a roar of applause.

I still remember my cousins and I being so exhilarated that we decided to run around and try everything that the carnival had to offer! We raced one another in bumper cars, rode on the giant musical carousel, took pictures with a clown at the photo booth, and shrieked when we saw our moms shrink as we rose higher and higher on the Ferris wheel. As we descended, we looked up to see the sky light up with fireworks! The thunderous thuds and whistles of the fireworks echoed the excitement we felt inside.

It was truly a spectacular day and we all chatted about our favourite parts and performers on the drive back home.

A. Unscramble the carnival words to fill in the blanks.

1. The ______________ clapped and cheered at the carnival.
   oatcpestrs

2. The ______________ travels to my city every summer.
   lvrnacia

3. I chose a white horse on the musical ______________ .
   scaorule

4. Julius wants to be a ______________ . That is why he is always throwing multiple balls into the air.
   ruglejg

5. We were afraid that the acrobat would fall during her ______________ performance.
   gtihtorep gkawlin

6. Anna could swing high up on the ______________ without any fear!
   ezapetr

7. The child bought a sweet ______________ and got in line to pay for his ______________ .
   octotn ydacn / etckti

B. Draw lines to match.

At the carnival:

entertainer •

entertainment •

- **ringmaster**
- **acrobat**
- **bumper cars**
- **carousel**
- **tightrope walking**
- **Ferris wheel**
- **juggler**
- **trapeze**
- **magician**
- **clown**
- **fireworks**

C. Match the carnival words with their definitions. Then complete what the carnival performers say with the correct words.

Carnival Word	Definition
1. stilt walking •	• a march including bands and floats
2. contortionist •	• using a pair of long poles with footrests to walk
3. puppet show •	• a person who can bend his or her body into unnatural positions
4. unicycle •	• a theatrical performance using inanimate objects controlled by wires
5. parade •	• a vehicle that looks like a bicycle but has only one wheel

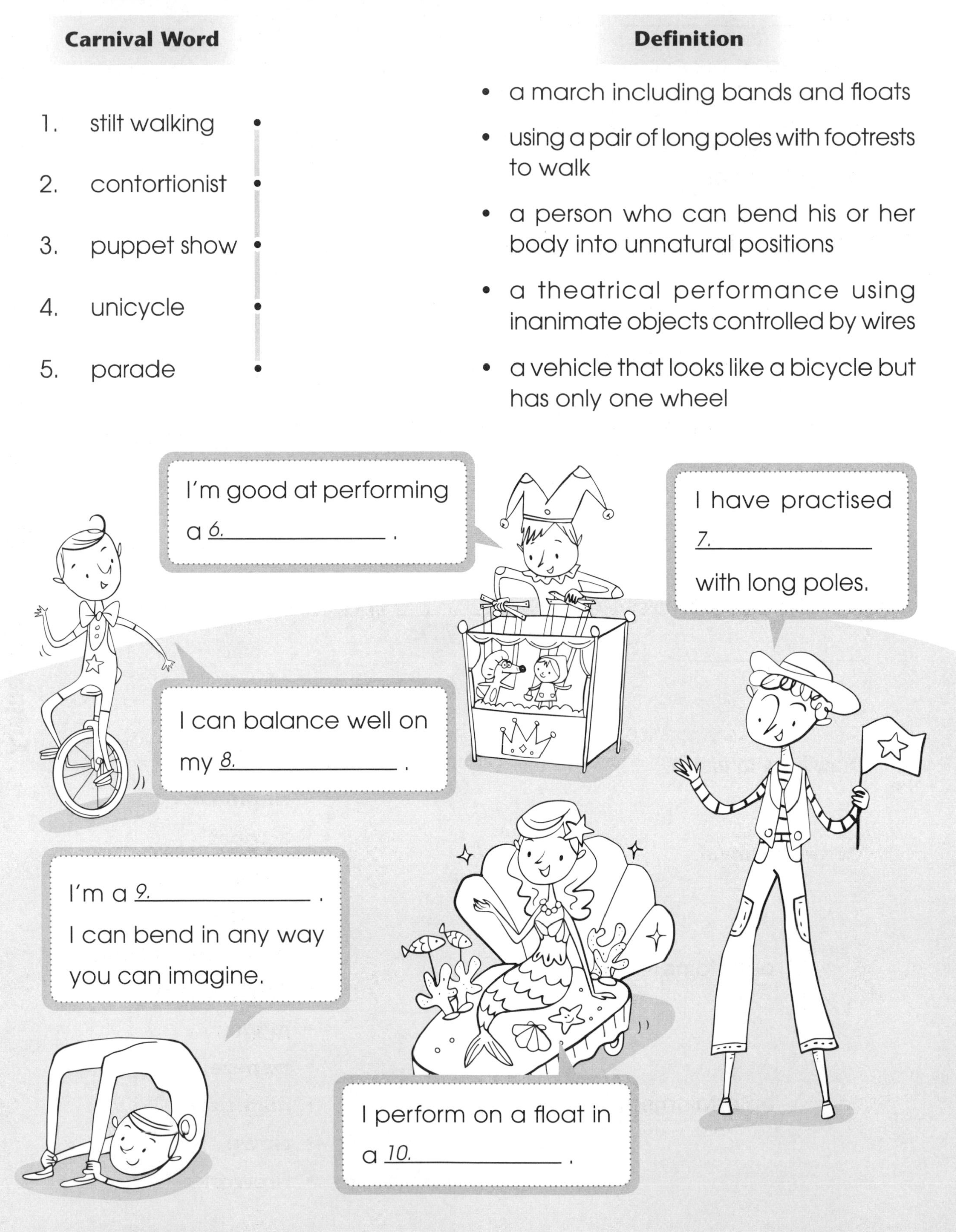

D. Use the picture clues to complete the crossword puzzle.

Carnival Words

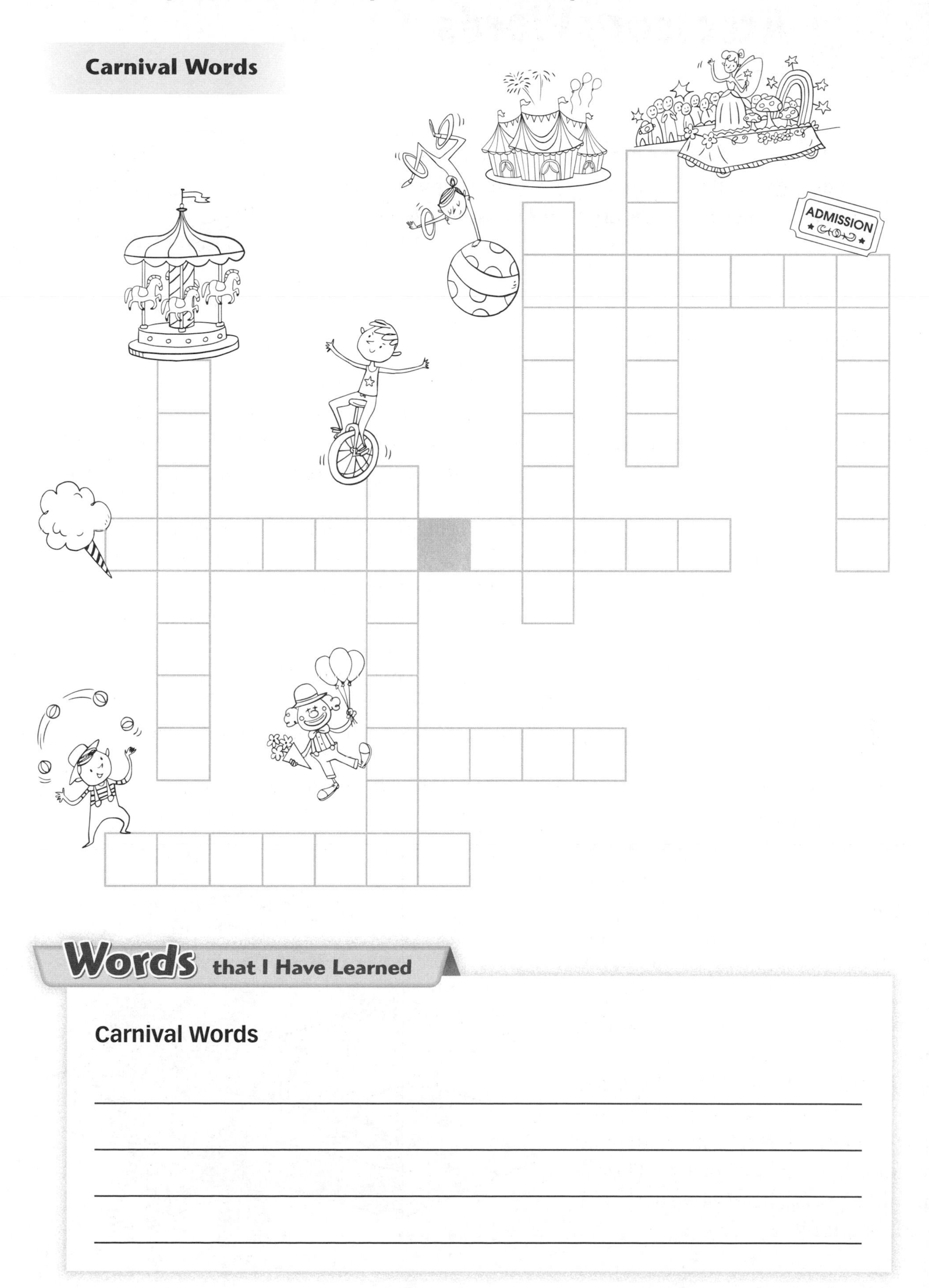

Words that I Have Learned

Carnival Words

Section 3 Vocabulary

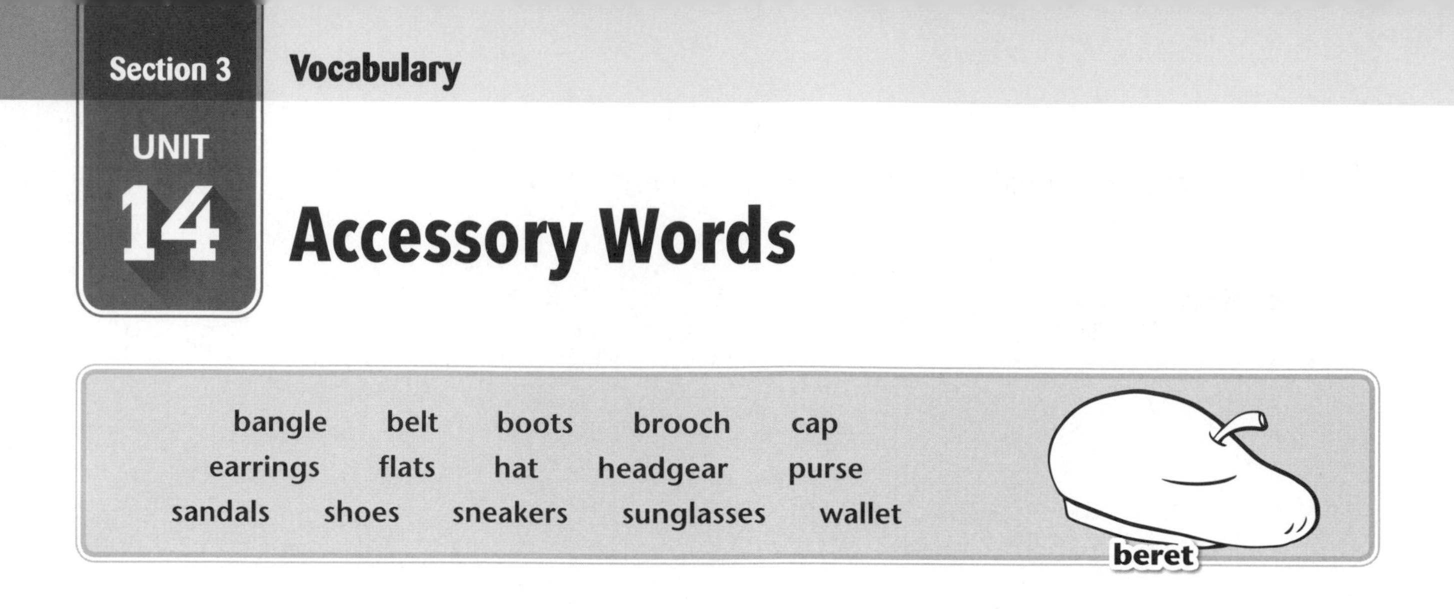

UNIT 14 Accessory Words

bangle belt boots brooch cap
earrings flats hat headgear purse
sandals shoes sneakers sunglasses wallet

Sunday Shopping

On bright spring Sundays, there was nothing Donna and Roy liked doing better than emptying their wallets to purchase cool new accessories at the mall. So, come Sunday, that is where they found themselves, ready to accessorize their ever-growing wardrobes.

Pushing her sunglasses back and untangling her hair out of her dangly earrings, Donna let out a sigh. "I really hope I can find new golden bangles to go with these earrings I got last week." She readjusted the strap of her purse on her shoulder. "Or maybe a new brooch for my jacket," she added thoughtfully as they walked past various shops.

"What you really need are new sandals," Roy said, taking off his navy cap and gazing at a display of sneakers through a shop window. "Be practical, Donna! The only types of shoes you have are running shoes, spring flats, and winter boots," he chuckled.

Donna rolled her eyes and smiled at him. "You could definitely use a new belt." She looked sympathetically at his brown leather belt. It definitely looked like it had seen better days. Out loud, she said, "You've worn yours out." Roy shook his head in disagreement. "No, it's still got a little bit of life left in it. What I really need today is a nice hat," he said. Donna looked at him funnily as she paused in front of a display of headgear. "What kind of hat? You have so many!" she questioned. "A beret," he responded reluctantly. "In late spring? There's nothing practical about that!" she said, laughing.

A. **Unscramble the words and fill in the blanks. Then match the words with their definitions. Write the letters.**

Accessory Word		Definition
1. ________ (letb)	☐	A type of women's shoes that are level at the bottom, usually worn in spring and summer
2. ________ (leltaw)	☐	B a piece of jewellery with a pin on the back that is secured to clothing
3. ________ (aunsgsless)	☐	C worn around the waist to support or adorn clothing
4. ________ (lftas)	☐	D a small, often foldable case for carrying paper money, coins, and credit cards
5. ________ (hcboro)	☐	E glasses with dark lens that protect your eyes from direct sunlight

B. **Solve the accessory word riddles.**

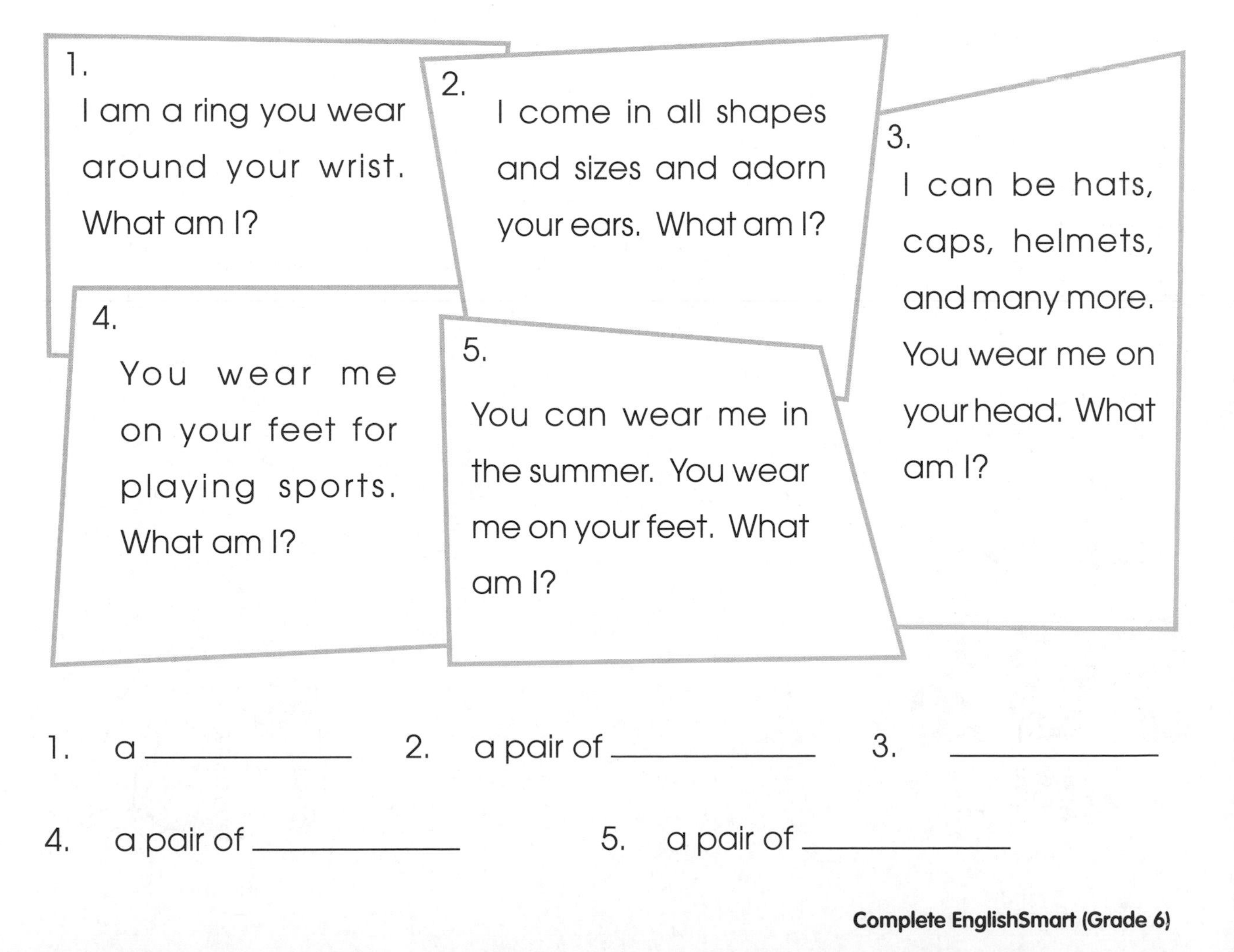

1. a ________ 2. a pair of ________ 3. ________

4. a pair of ________ 5. a pair of ________

Section 3 Vocabulary

C. **Fill in the blanks with the correct winter accessory words.**

Winter Accessory Words

boots earmuffs glove mittens
scarf shawls toque

D. **Write the accessory words under the correct headings. Then give one more example for each and draw a picture to go with it.**

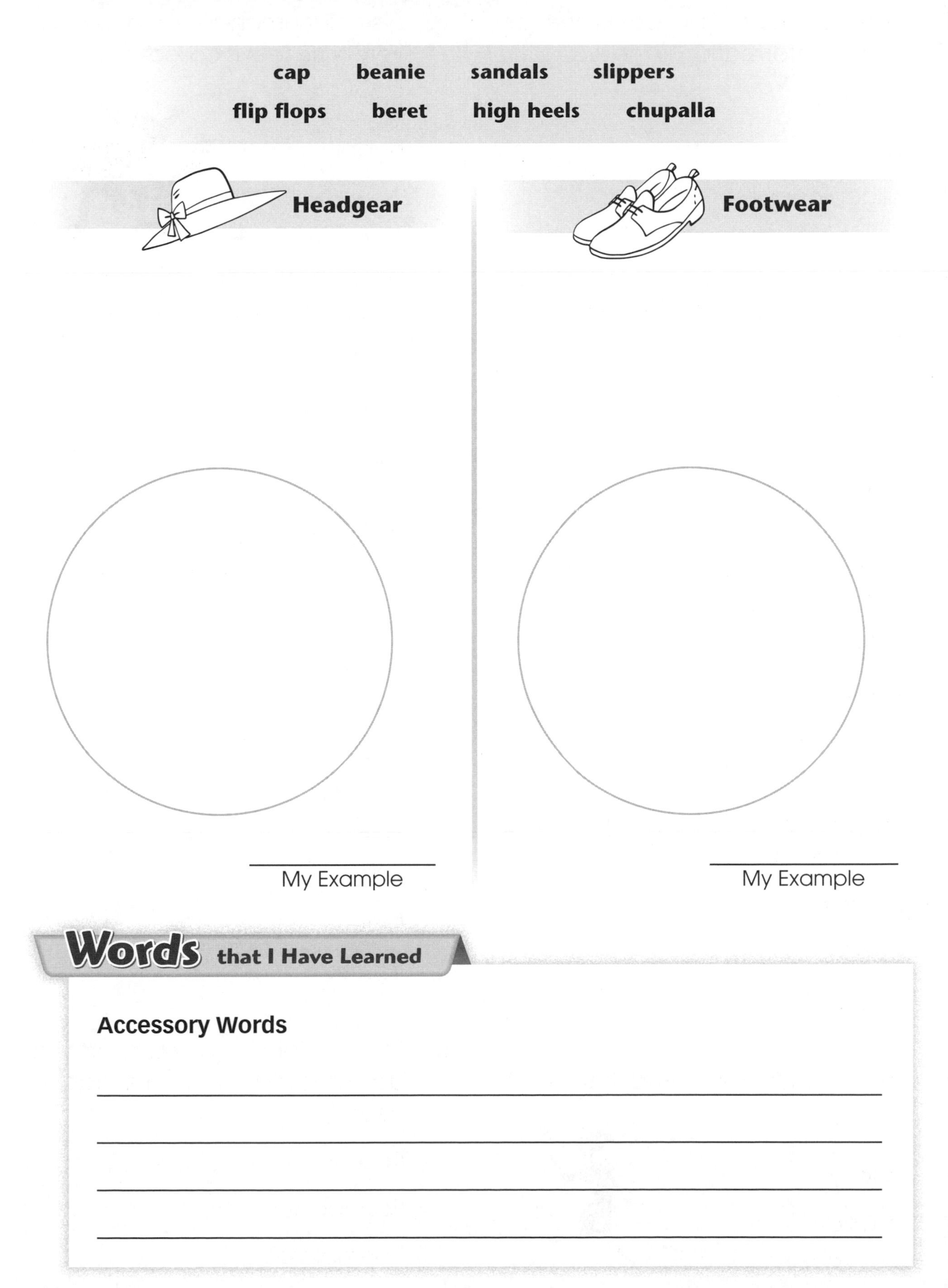

Words that I Have Learned

Accessory Words

A. Circle the answers.

1. The capacity of the computer for storing information is the ______ .

   transistor

   memory

   silicon chip

2. What was the common unit of measurement used on farms in England?

   acre

   yard

   furlong

3. The British were the originators of the ______ system.

   metric

   non-metric

   standard

4. The marathon run is a difficult test of physical ______ .

   routine

   training

   endurance

5. Which fantasy creature is this?

   an elf

   a fairy

   a wizard

6. A small, human-like creature with very hairy feet is called a ______ .

   troll

   hobbit

7. What is a technique used in hockey to fool opponents?

   a hat-trick

   a rebound

   a deke

8. What are two or more letters joined together referred to as?

   a ligature

   a script

   a text

9. "Gothic" refers to a type of ______ .

   text

   font

   flourish

10. The first landmass that formed about a billion years ago is called ______ .

    Rodinia

    Pangaea

    Panthalassa

11. Which dessert is served best with cream sauce poured over it?

semifreddo

baklava

malva pudding

12. What does MVP stand for?

Most Vital Player

Most Valuable Player

Most Valuable Position

13. Which constellation depicts Orpheus's musical instrument?

Lyra

Ursa Major

Cassiopeia

14. The North Star is another name for ______ .

Orion

Cassiopeia

Polaris

15. ______ your time in service of a cause if you are unable to donate.

Volunteer

Endow

Raise

16. Which of the following does not endorse living sustainably?

recycling and reusing

using the dishwasher

hanging your clothes to dry

17. To conserve means "to ______".

avoid wasteful use of

discard of

expend

18. What is a common ride found at carnivals?

a roller coaster

a Ferris wheel

a water slide

19. Berets are ______ .

bags

hats

shoes

20. What type of footwear is worn only in the summer?

flip-flops

flats

running shoes

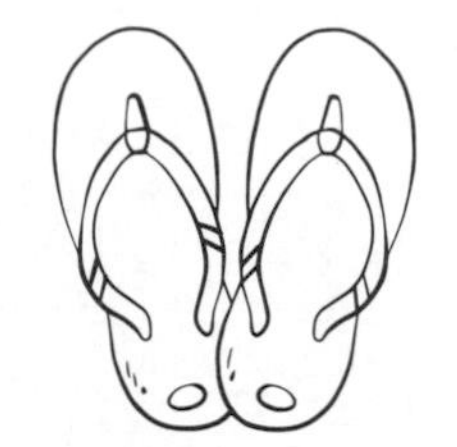

Physical, Hockey, and Baseball Words

B. Unscramble the words to complete the sentences. Then circle them in the word search.

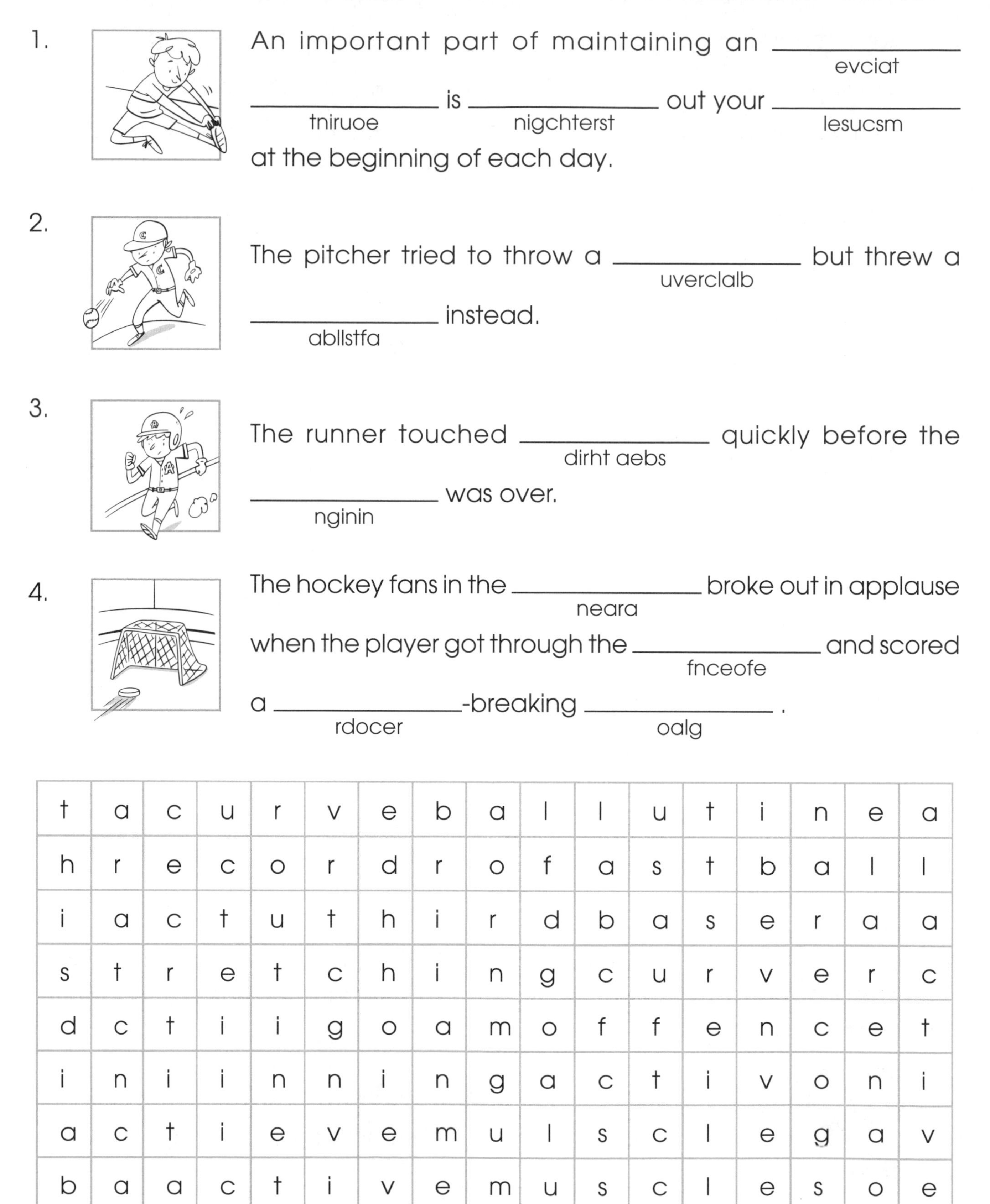

1. An important part of maintaining an ________ (evciat) ________ (tniruoe) is ________ (nigchterst) out your ________ (lesucsm) at the beginning of each day.

2. The pitcher tried to throw a ________ (uverclalb) but threw a ________ (abllstfa) instead.

3. The runner touched ________ (dirht aebs) quickly before the ________ (nginin) was over.

4. The hockey fans in the ________ (neara) broke out in applause when the player got through the ________ (fnceofe) and scored a ________ (rdocer)-breaking ________ (oalg).

t	a	c	u	r	v	e	b	a	l	l	u	t	i	n	e	a
h	r	e	c	o	r	d	r	o	f	a	s	t	b	a	l	l
i	a	c	t	u	t	h	i	r	d	b	a	s	e	r	a	a
s	t	r	e	t	c	h	i	n	g	c	u	r	v	e	r	c
d	c	t	i	i	g	o	a	m	o	f	f	e	n	c	e	t
i	n	i	i	n	n	i	n	g	a	c	t	i	v	o	n	i
a	c	t	i	e	v	e	m	u	l	s	c	l	e	g	a	v
b	a	a	c	t	i	v	e	m	u	s	c	l	e	s	o	e

C. Unscramble the computer, fantasy, and book words to complete the story.

Juliet came back from the library with a new book each week. She knew she could use her computer to order books 1. ______________ (neilon) with a simple click of her 2. ______________ (ouesm). In fact, she had dozens of books 3. ______________ (oaowndlded) already. But there was something special about reading a physical copy of a book that could not be replaced by reading from a 4. ______________ (oronmit). So, she would spend hours browsing through the library racks until she found a book that interested her.

Today, her love of 5. ______________ (terureatli) had her roaming through the fantasy section. As she scanned her eyes over the beautiful 6. ______________ (straillutsion) on the covers, a book with images of various alluring 7. ______________ (thycalim) ______________ (eatruescr) caught her attention. Though she was not familiar with the 8. ______________ (throua) of the book, she keenly read over the brief 9. ______________ (ynposiss) before eagerly checking it out.

That night, Juliet sat on her bed rapt in reading the 10. ______________ (oicreh) feats of *Diana the* 11. ______________ (sMteron) *-slayer*, the brave girl who fought valiantly to free her land from the control of an evil 12. ______________ (dizwar) and his fearsome fire-breathing 13. ______________ (ragdno). So absorbed was she in her reading that she did not notice it was dawn, and the whole night had passed her by.

Dessert, Charity, and Carnival Words

cremeschnitte
soufflé
semifreddo
gulab jamun

D. Write the correct dessert words under the pictures. Then underline all the charity words.

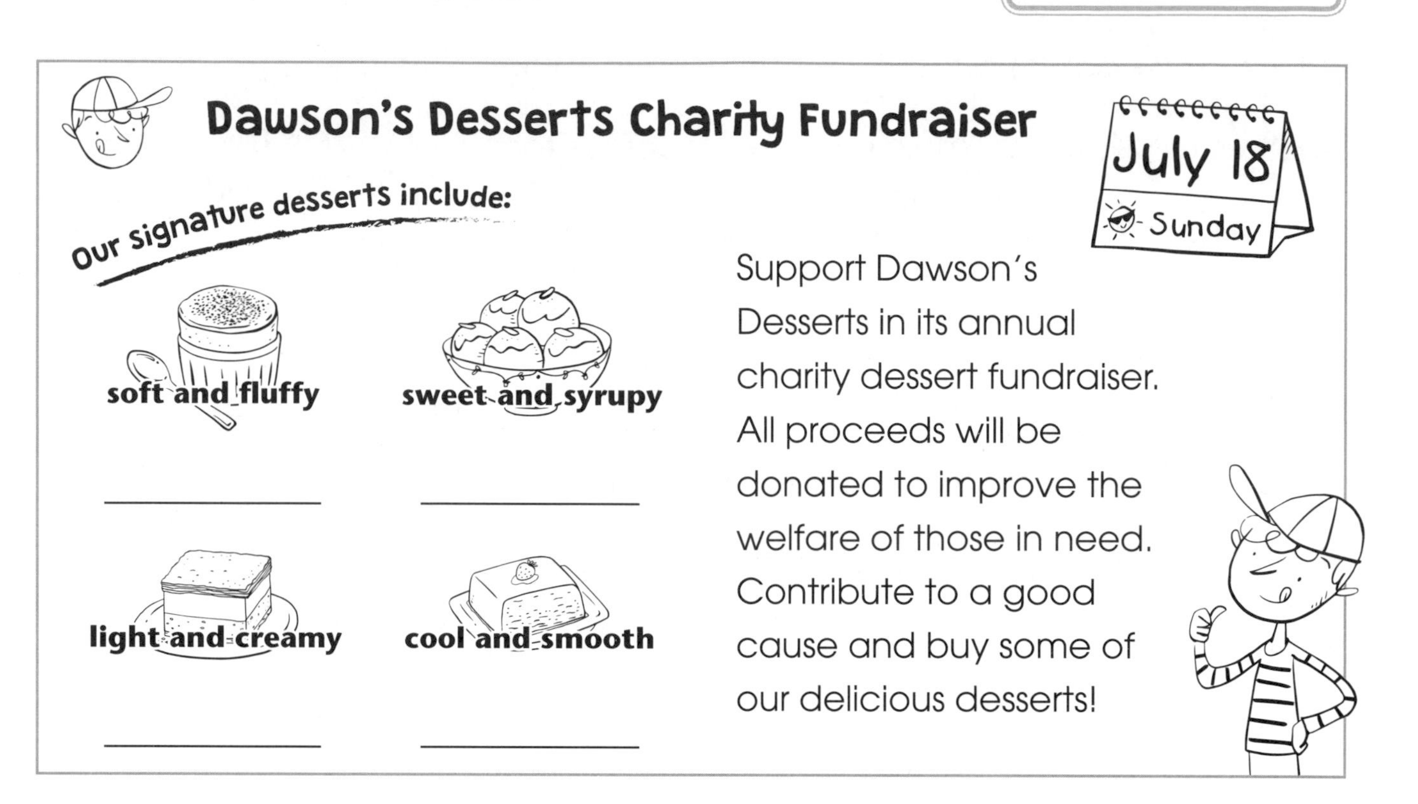

E. Put the words in order to form sentences. Then circle the carnival words.

1. accomplished the acrobat and feats the contortionist amazing

____

2. watched cotton candy as we ate the fireworks we

____

3. fun as almost the Ferris wheel were as the bumper cars

____

4. spectator stage on final act the magician brought a for his

____

5. another juggling as clown a stilt walking clown was was

____

Geography and Constellation Words

F. Match the words with the correct descriptions.

1. landform •	• one big global ocean that surrounded Pangaea
2. archipelago •	• the way a region looks on the surface of the Earth
3. continental drift •	• the supercontinent that existed millions of years ago
4. Panthalassa •	• hills, valleys, canyons, plains, and basins are examples of this
5. Pangaea •	• a group of islands on a stretch of water
6. topography •	• slow movement of the continental plates on the Earth's surface

G. Identify and write the names of the constellations.

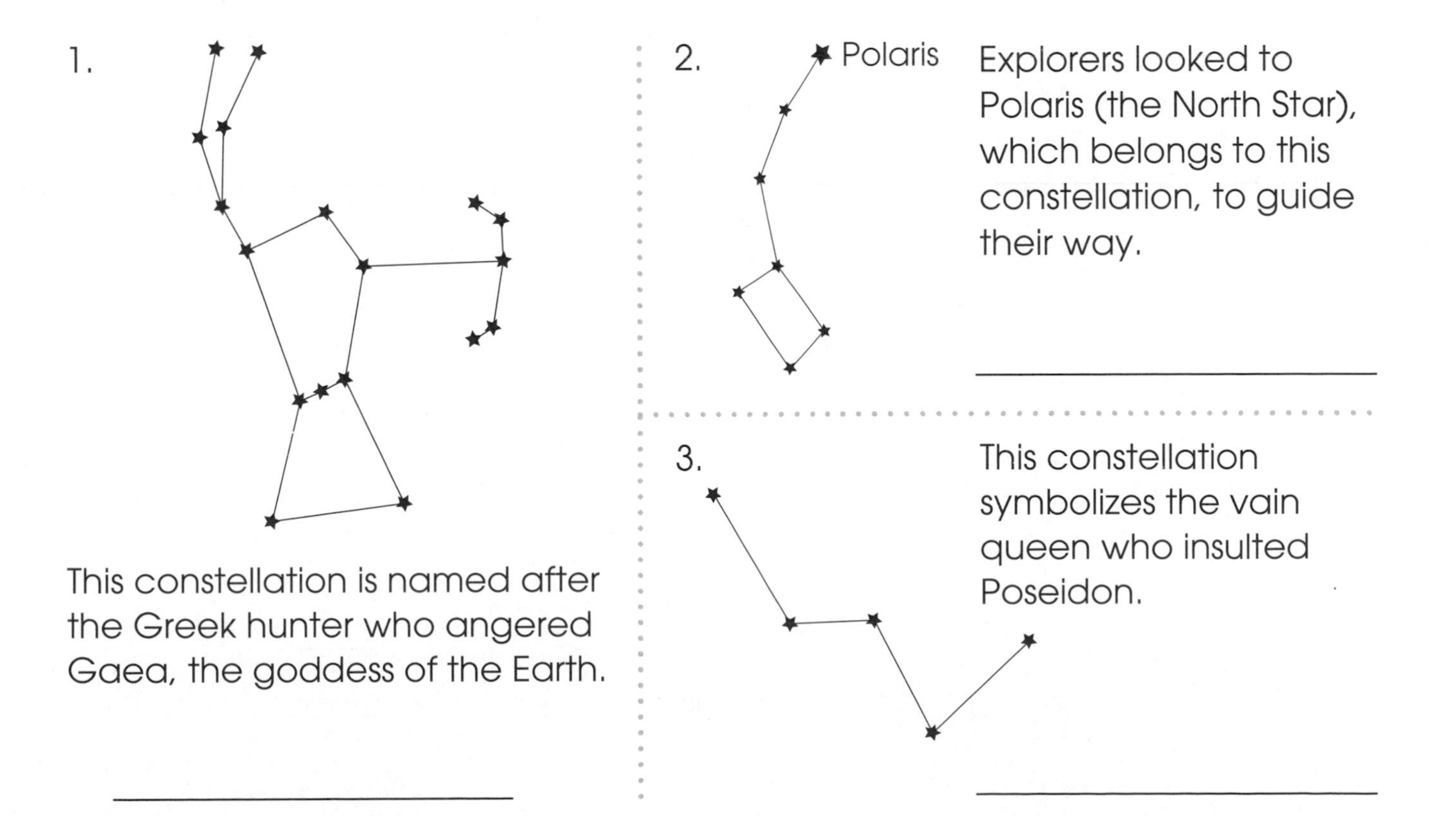

1. This constellation is named after the Greek hunter who angered Gaea, the goddess of the Earth.

____

2. Explorers looked to Polaris (the North Star), which belongs to this constellation, to guide their way.

____

3. This constellation symbolizes the vain queen who insulted Poseidon.

____

Section 4

Reading and Writing

UNIT 1 The Gordian Knot

In ancient times, there was a kingdom called Phrygia, which is modern day Turkey. One day, the Phrygians found themselves without a king as the last king had died without producing an heir. The oracle of Telmissus, however, declared to the people that the next man to enter the city in an ox cart should be named the new king.

That man was Gordias. He was a peasant, and when he drove his ox cart into the city, the Phrygians instantly proclaimed him king and renamed the kingdom Gordium in his honour. To show his gratitude, Gordias dedicated his ox cart to the Phrygian god Sabazios and tied it to a pillar in an incredibly elaborate knot.

Many years passed and the ox cart stayed tied to the pillar. One day, the oracle made another prophecy. It said that whosoever unravelled the intricate knot would rule all of Asia. Upon hearing the legend of the Gordian Knot, Alexander the Great travelled to Gordium to untie the knot. Many men had come to try before him but they had all failed. Alexander himself had great difficulty in untying the knot, so he unsheathed his sword and cut the knot in half. Alexander the Great broke the Gordian Knot that had confounded so many before him. He then went on to conquer most of Asia, fulfilling the prophecy.

Due to the way Alexander unravelled the knot, the phrase "Gordian knot" has become a metaphor for an intractable problem solved by a bold solution.

A. Circle the answers.

1. Where is Phrygia located?

   in Telmissus

   in Turkey

   in Asia

2. Where is the oracle from?

   Phrygia

   Turkey

   Telmissus

3. To whom does Gordias dedicate his ox cart?

   Alexander the Great

   an oracle

   a Phrygian god

4. How many prophecies does the oracle make?

   one

   two

   three

A metaphor is a figure of speech that describes something in a way that is not true in order to give an explanation or suggest a resemblance to something else.

B. Answer the questions.

1. What is the metaphor in the legend?

   ____

   ____

2. What happens when Gordias enters the city in his ox cart?

   ____

   ____

3. What is the oracle's second prophecy?

   ____

   ____

4. How does Alexander the Great "unravel" the Gordian Knot?

   ____

   ____

C. Read the legend. Then answer the questions.

The Legend of King Arthur

Arthur was the first born son of King Uther and therefore the heir to the throne. A wizard named Merlin advised the king and queen to hide Arthur's true identity so that enemies would never find him. Years later, upon the death of King Uther, chaos descended upon the kingdom until, at last, young Arthur was able to pull the Sword in the Stone, which Merlin had placed there using magic to prove who the true heir and rightful king was. Arthur gathered around him faithful knights and together they fought the Saxons, who were invading their lands.

King Arthur lived in Camelot with Queen Guinevere and his knights. He received the sword Excalibur from a sorceress called the Lady of the Lake, and with this weapon, he defeated many enemies. Sadly, peace did not last forever and in the Battle of Camlann, against the evil Mordred, King Arthur was mortally wounded and taken to the mystical island of Avalon.

Elements of a Legend

1. Write the characters in the correct category.

Protagonist	Antagonist

A protagonist is a leading character. An antagonist is an opponent or adversary of the protagonist.

2. When he becomes king, what is Arthur's main plight?

____

3. What are the magical elements in this legend?

____

____

4. It is said that Arthur was based on a real man. Do some research and write who the real Arthur might have been.

____

D. Write a short legend.

Don't forget that a legend is loosely based on a real person, event, or place. Legends usually have magical elements and are full of action!

The Legend of ______________________________

____

____

____

____

____

____

____

____

____

____

____

____

____

Words that I Have Learned

____

____

____

UNIT 2

Dandelion

One day, on my emerald
patch of lawn,
When the sun was climbing,
soon after dawn,
And not long after 5
an early spring shower
stood a guest, uninvited:
a yellow flower.

It must have been lonely,
that flower head, 10
'cause the grass soon looked
like a flower bed.
The greenest of all
the neighbourhood plots,
was tarnished with yellow 15
polka dots.

At first I tried
to pluck the blooms
to put in vases
in all the rooms. 20
But in the house
the flowers died
while on the lawn
they multiplied.

My neighbours missed 25
that stretch of green.
"Restore the turf!"
"Bring back pristine!"
And there they stood,
angry and red, 30
in front of my unplanned
flower bed.

Then much to my
and my neighbours' surprise
the flowers turned white 35
and took to the skies.
They must have known
they weren't welcome here.
I wonder, will they
be back next year? 40

It's spring again
and what is new?
Dandelions!
Where grass once grew!
On every lawn 45
a sea of gold.
Dandy? Dandy!
NOT, I'm told.

A. Circle the answers.

1. What type of narrative is this text?

   a short story

   a poem

   a legend

2. How many stanzas does this text have?

   six

   eight

   ten

   A stanza is a group of lines in a poem.

3. What does "tarnished" in Line 15 mean?

   polished

   decorated

   stained

4. What are the "yellow polka dots" in Lines 15 – 16?

   yellow ladybugs

   bumblebees

   dandelions

B. Answer the questions.

1. How is this a narrative poem?

   ____

   ____

A narrative poem is a poem that tells a story.

2. How do the speaker's neighbours feel about the dandelions? Why?

   ____

   ____

3. Do the dandelions return the next year? When?

   ____

4. How does the narrator describe dandelions in the last stanza? Why?

   ____

   ____

   ____

C. Read the acrostic poem and answer the questions. Then complete the poems.

> An acrostic poem is a poem in which the first letter of each line spells a word or a phrase when read downward. The lines do not need to rhyme.

Dandelion

Drifting
Aloft, in
No

Direction,
Easy
Landing.
In like a lamb, but
Out like a lion. A
Neighbourhood Zoo

1. What is the acrostic poem about?

____

2.

CANDY

Crunchy treats
A______________________
Nutty and sweet
D______________________
Yummy to eat

3.

SCHOOL

So much to know
C______________________
H______________________
O______________________
O______________________
Love learning

D. Write a narrative poem or an acrostic poem.

Title: ________________________________

____

____

____

____

____

____

____

____

____

____

____

____

____

____

____

____

____

____

If you are writing a narrative poem, make sure to have a beginning, a middle, and an end like a story. If you are writing an acrostic poem, don't forget to use words that will give the reader strong images of what you are writing about.

Words that I Have Learned

____

____

____

UNIT 3

The Bully

One morning, Mia had just arrived at her new school when she suddenly felt a strong shove from behind her.

"Move!" a girl yelled and then walked away.

At school in Ms. Winter's class, Mia was telling her classmates a little about herself when she recognized the girl who had shoved her sitting in the back. Mia began to shake nervously and quickly finished talking.

When the lunch bell rang, everyone got up to get their lunch. Mia's mom had prepared an egg salad sandwich, Mia's favourite, but before she could take a bite, the scary girl knocked it off her desk and onto the floor.

"Oops," she said. Again, the girl walked away. Mia was too scared to say anything and for the next two weeks, the girl did it again and again.

One day, Mia had had enough. Before the girl could walk away, Mia spoke up. "Stop it! I bet you don't know how it feels to be hungry," Mia told her, scared but defiant. The girl looked at her coldly and said, "Yes, I do."

And then Mia realized something – the scary girl never ate lunch. She just walked around bothering other students but Mia never saw her eat. This made Mia sad. "Maybe that's why she knocks over my lunch," she thought. "She's jealous." Mia thought about how she could help the girl and talked to her mother about it. "Oh no, that's not good. Nobody should go hungry," said her mother. "I have an idea! You can give her a sandwich tomorrow to show her that you understand."

The next day, as soon as the lunch bell rang, Mia stood up and sat next to the girl. The girl looked at her in bewilderment as Mia handed her a sandwich. The girl was silent but, slowly, she picked up the sandwich and took a bite. Mia smiled widely and began eating her sandwich happily beside the scary girl. The best part, Mia thought, was the small smile on the girl's face as she took another bite of her sandwich, and another, and another.

A. Circle the answers.

1. Where does the bully sit in class?

   in the front

   by the window

   in the back

2. What is Mia's favourite lunch food?

   tuna sandwich

   egg salad sandwich

   chicken sandwich

3. How does the bully feel about Mia's lunch?

   mad

   jealous

   happy

4. How does Mia feel at the end of the story?

   sad

   happy

   angry

The theme of a story is the main idea that the writer wants to convey to his or her readers.

B. Answer the questions.

1. What is the theme of this short story?

   ____

   ____

2. Who are the characters in this short story?

   ____

3. Why is the bully jealous of Mia?

   ____

   ____

4. What solution does Mia find to the problem?

   ____

   ____

C. Think of a story you would like to write. Complete the chart.

Five Elements of a Short Story

A short story has five elements: theme, plot, setting, characters, and point of view.

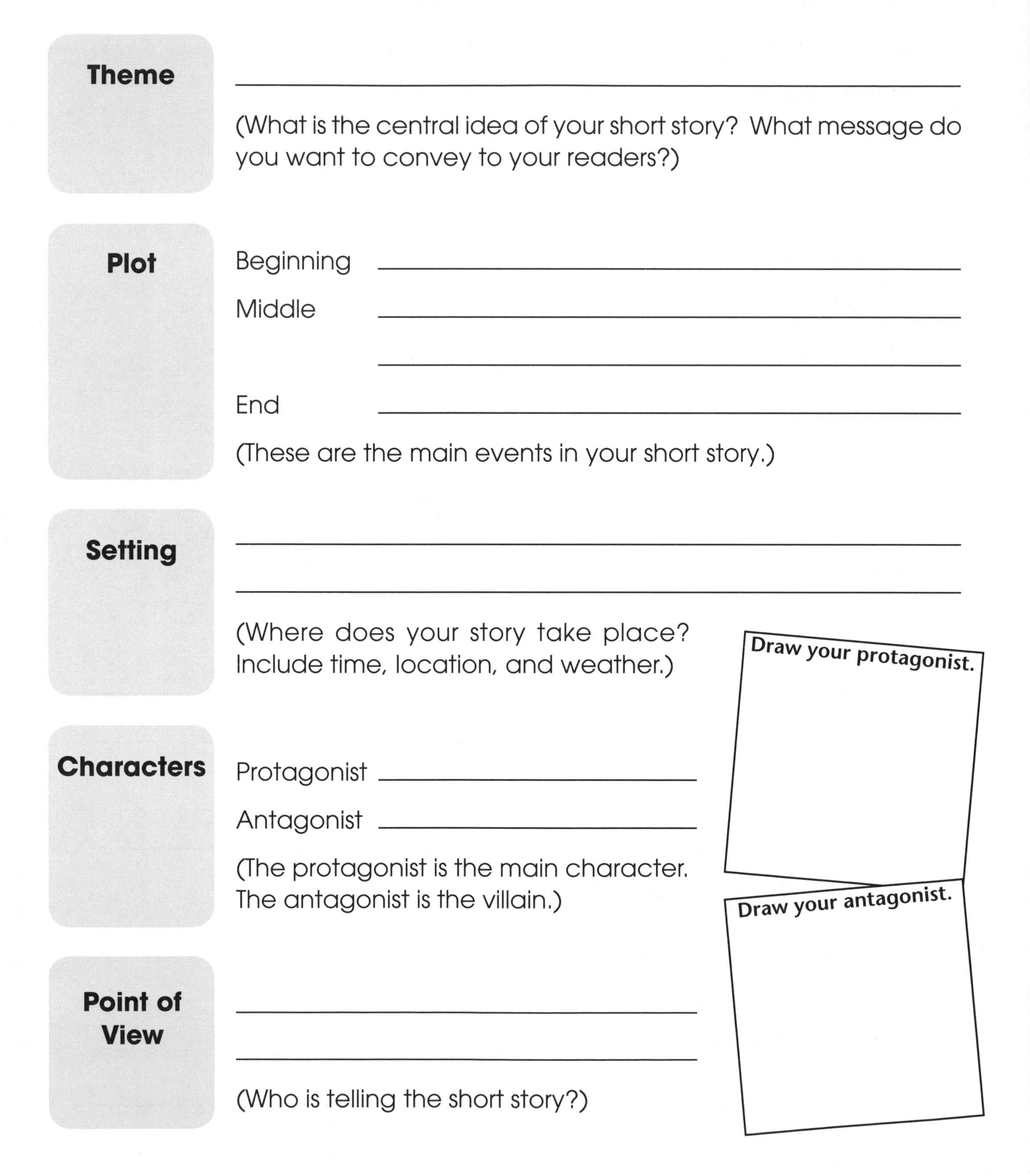

Theme

____

(What is the central idea of your short story? What message do you want to convey to your readers?)

Plot

Beginning ________________________________

Middle ________________________________

____

End ________________________________

(These are the main events in your short story.)

Setting

____

____

(Where does your story take place? Include time, location, and weather.)

Characters

Protagonist ________________________

Antagonist ________________________

(The protagonist is the main character. The antagonist is the villain.)

Point of View

____

____

(Who is telling the short story?)

Draw your protagonist.

Draw your antagonist.

D. **Write a short story using the information from (C).**

Don't forget to include all five of the elements of a short story.

Title: ______________________

____

____

____

____

____

____

____

____

____

____

____

____

____

____

____

____

Words that I Have Learned

____

____

____

UNIT 4

The Beauties and the Boastful King

King Alfonso had a wife named Queen Jadah and a daughter named Princess Kallithea. Their beauty was so renowned that people came from all over the world to the Kingdom of Fanta to witness it. So proud and boastful was King Alfonso of their beauty that he announced a day of celebration dedicated to his wife and daughter.

But one king, King Humza, was insulted by King Alfonso's pretentious claim. "Only a goddess may have a day of celebration dedicated to her!" he cried angrily. And so, to teach this pompous king a lesson, King Humza took matters into his own hands and devised a plan.

On the day of the celebration, every man, woman, and child lined the streets to revel in the beauty of the queen and the princess. As the two women waved to the people, a hooded figure stepped in front of their carriage, halting the march. Nobody had ever seen him before and the crowd wondered who this ominous man was.

"Who are you?" King Alfonso demanded.

"I am a messenger," the hooded man answered. "I was sent by a man who believes your priorities are aimless and misguided. He wants you to learn otherwise." As he spoke, he pulled his hands out from under his cloak and produced two round shells.

"It's witch's fire! Run!" a woman from the crowd exclaimed. This made the crowd disperse in horror as many had heard about or witnessed the destructive effects of witch's fire. Witch's fire was magical fire. It was brighter than the sun and burned hotter than any flame on earth.

King Alfonso watched in horror as the hooded man threw the witch's fire at his wife and daughter. Without thinking, he threw himself in front of them. Astonishingly, the fire appeared to be ordinary and his soldiers were able to extinguish it. King Alfonso, however, was left blind and unable to ever look upon the beauty of his queen and princess.

"It's alright, my dears," he told them as they cried. "For it is your hearts I most treasure."

A. Circle the answers.

1. What is the setting of the story?

   Humza

   Fanta

   Jadah

2. Who is the boastful king?

   Humza

   Alfonso

   the hooded man

3. Who halts the march?

   a hooded figure

   King Humza

   the crowd of people

4. What does the hooded man do?

   falls down

   throws witch's fire

   scares the horse

A fantasy story is set in an imaginary land and involves the supernatural.

B. Answer the questions.

1. What is the fantasy element of this story?

   ____

   ____

2. What is King Humza insulted by?

   ____

   ____

3. What is witch's fire?

   ____

   ____

4. What lesson does King Alfonso learn at the end of the story?

   ____

   ____

C. Complete the chart for a fantasy story that you will write.

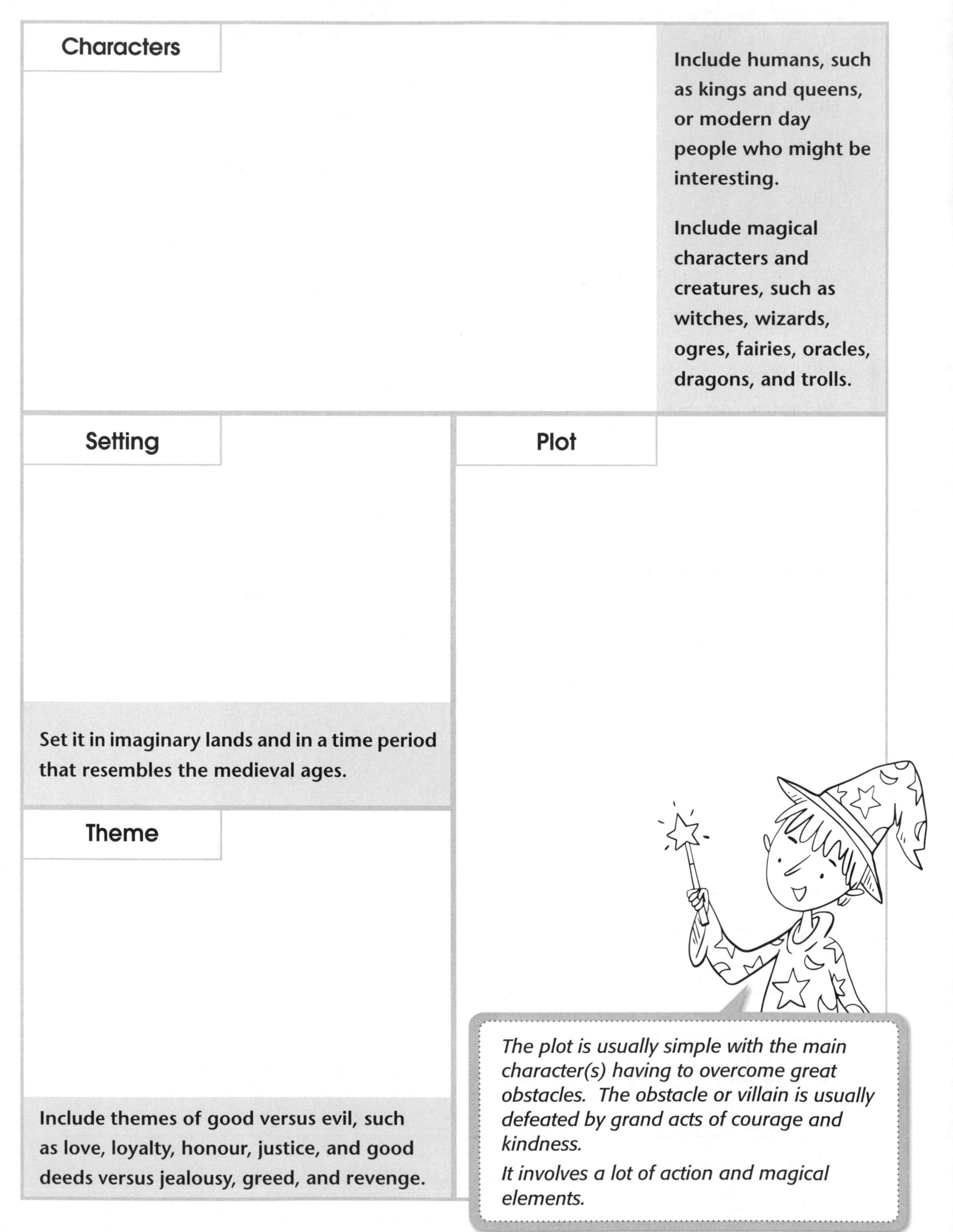

D. **Write a fantasy story using your ideas from (C).**

Title

Fantasy stories can also be set in the modern day. Harry Potter, for example, is based in this century but still involves traditional fantasy elements.

Words that I Have Learned

UNIT 5

Andromeda and Perseus

In Greek mythology, Andromeda was a princess, the daughter of King Cepheus and Queen Cassiopeia of Aethiopia. Queen Cassiopeia was a beautiful but vain woman. One day, she committed hubris, which is the characteristic of having foolish pride, by saying that her daughter, Andromeda, was more beautiful than the Nereids, the nymph-daughters of Nereus and Doris and companions of the god of the sea, Poseidon.

Angered by the claim, Poseidon sent a sea monster named Cetus to ravage the lands of Aethiopia. King Cepheus and Queen Cassiopeia decided to consult the oracle who advised them that the only way to appease the wrath of Poseidon and save their kingdom was to sacrifice Andromeda. And so Andromeda was chained to a sea cliff waiting to be devoured by the sea monster.

Fortunately, Perseus, the son of Danaë and the Greek god Zeus, was flying by on his winged horse, Pegasus. Perseus is famously known for proving his bravery by slaying the monster Medusa. As he came across Andromeda chained to a rock, he fell in love with her. He approached the parents of the beautiful princess with an offer to rescue their daughter if they promised to allow him to marry her. They agreed. Therefore, when Cetus emerged from the water, looking forward to a delicious meal, Perseus immediately killed the beast by driving his sword into the monster's back.

Afterwards, Perseus married Andromeda and together they returned to Greece and had seven sons and one daughter. According to Greek mythology, the descendants of Perseus and Andromeda went on to rule Mycenae, one of the most prosperous towns in the Mycenaean times. Also, Heracles, a famous Greek hero, and Perses – who is believed to be the ancestor of the Persian race – were both descendants of Perseus and Andromeda.

However, Poseidon, not wanting Cassiopeia to escape punishment, placed her in the heavens, chained to a throne to revolve upside down for eternity. The goddess Athena also placed Perseus and Andromeda in the heavens after their deaths. All three figures are constellations that can be seen in the northern sky.

A. Circle the answers.

1. Where does this myth take place?

   in Greece

   in Aethiopia

   in Egypt

2. What is hubris?

   foolish pride

   anger

   beauty

3. What is the name of the sea monster?

   Nereus

   Pegasus

   Cetus

4. Where can the constellations of Andromeda and Perseus be seen?

   in Aethiopia

   in the northern sky

   in Greece

B. Answer the questions.

Myths were written for many purposes, one of which was to teach moral lessons or set moral standards through the stories.

1. What is the moral lesson of this myth?

   ____

   ____

2. What do the king and queen of Aethiopia do to appease Poseidon's wrath?

   ____

   ____

3. Why does Perseus want to save Andromeda from the sea monster?

   ____

   ____

4. Is Cassiopeia ultimately punished for her vanity? How?

   ____

   ____

C. Research and read another myth. Then answer the questions.

Some myths were written to give explanations to life and natural phenomena (e.g. Zeus was the god of thunder) and to explain social customs.

1. Write a summary of the myth.

____
____
____
____
____
____
____

2. What is the setting of the myth?

____

3. Identify the characters in the myth.

God/Goddess	Mortal	Other Magical Creature
____________	____________	____________
____________	____________	____________
____________	____________	____________
____________	____________	____________

4. What phenomenon or moral lesson does the myth explain or teach?

____
____

D. **Write your own myth.**

Myths always explain something about the universe, whether it is about human emotions, the natural world, or the culture on which the myth is based.

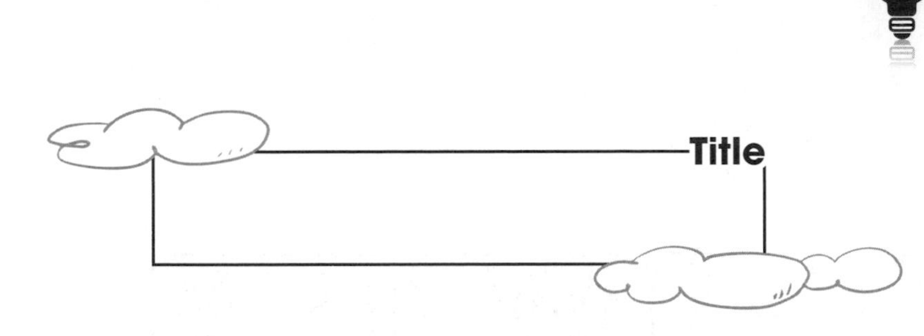

Words that I Have Learned

UNIT 6 Super Boys

A. Circle the answers.

1. What are the boys' superhero names?

   Super Lads

   Super Boys

   Super Kids

2. What contest is their neighbourhood trying to win?

   a cleanliness contest

   a beauty contest

   a cooperation contest

3. What do the boys do "wrong"?

   They break the garbage lids.

   They mismatch the garbage lids.

   They do not pick up the garbage lids.

4. What does their neighbourhood win for?

   originality and creativity

   organization and cleanliness

   orderliness and creativity

B. Answer the questions.

In a graphic novel, a panel is a segment or box that contains images and text. Sometimes, a panel also contains a caption, which provides information about the scene told by the narrator.

1. How many panels does this page in a graphic novel have?

   ____

2. What does the caption in the first panel tell the reader?

   ____

   ____

3. What is the purpose of the speech bubbles?

   ____

4. How do the Super Boys help their neighbourhood?

   ____

   ____

C. **Brainstorm ideas for a four-panel scene in a graphic novel that you will create. Then sketch the characters and setting.**

Brainstorm

Plot:

Characters:

Setting:

Dialogue:

Sketch

Characters:

Setting:

D. **Create a four-panel scene in a graphic novel using your ideas from (C).**

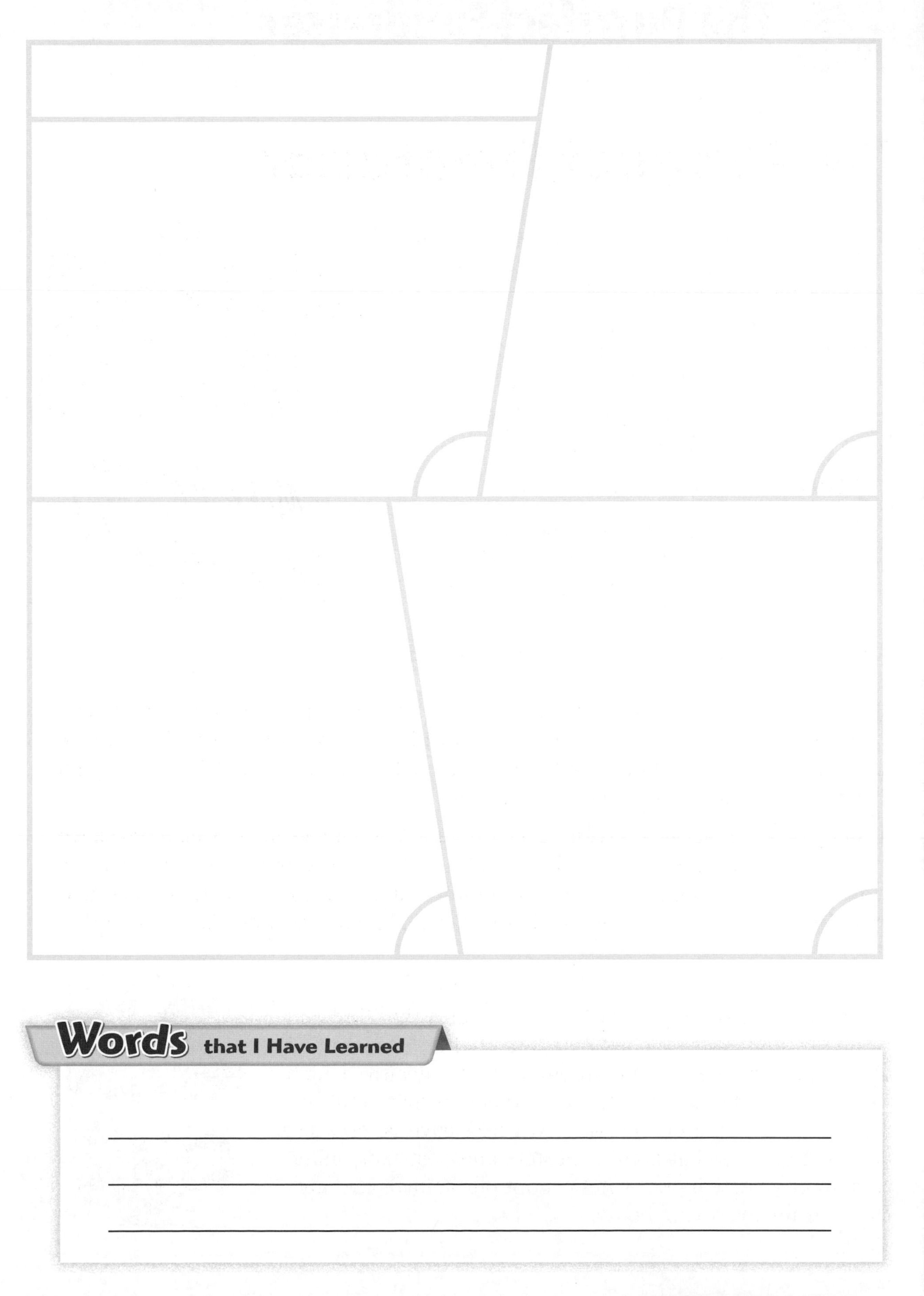

Words that I Have Learned

UNIT 7

The Purrrfect Fundraiser

The Purrrfect Fundraiser

The dedicated team at Purrrfect Pets Animal Shelter is proud to announce the details of our Annual Purrrfect Fundraiser!

What: The Purrrfect Pets Animal Shelter's Annual Purrrfect Fundraiser

When: Saturday, August 17, 2019 from 11 a.m. to 5 p.m.

Where: Sunnyside Community Park

Why: To help spread awareness about the problems faced by countless abandoned and neglected animals all over our city

How: Buy tickets – $15 per adult/$5 per child

Make Your Day Purrrfect!

Take part in the various activities we have arranged for you and your family throughout the day: get your face painted with your favourite pet and learn how to create a 3-D model of your favourite animal! Plus, there will be snacks and drinks to get you through the fun-filled day!

Proceeds will go toward saving and caring for the homeless and sick animals we have rescued over the years. In order to make all of this possible, we rely on donations, government grants, and helpful volunteers to spend their time and resources to help reduce the number of sick and homeless animals in our city!

Purrrfect Pets employs special rescue teams that find and bring lost animals to the safety of our shelter. Our trained vets and staff help nurse them back to health, which includes providing them with the medication, love, and care that they desperately need. We also have a creative advertising team that creates posters and posts ads online to help prospective pet owners adopt our animals and give them a safe and loving home.

A. Circle the answers.

1. What is the name of the animal shelter?

   Pets Animal Shelter

   Purrrfect Animal Shelter

   Purrrfect Pets Animal Shelter

2. Where will the fundraiser be held?

   at the animal shelter

   at a community park

   at a carnival

3. How long will the fundraiser last?

   five hours

   six hours

   seven hours

4. Who creates posters and posts ads online?

   the advertising team

   the veterinarians

   the rescue team

The purpose of an ad is the overall message that the company or organization wants to convey to the readers.

B. Answer the questions.

1. What is the purpose of this ad?

   ____

   ____

2. What activities can people do at the fundraiser?

   ____

   ____

3. What will the proceeds from the fundraiser be used for?

   ____

   ____

4. What do the vets and staff provide for the animals at the shelter?

   ____

   ____

C. Read the ad and answer the questions.

1. What is the purpose of this ad?

   ____

2. What is the ad's slogan?

   ____

   ____

A slogan is a short but striking phrase.

3. How do the font size and style make the ad more effective?

   ____

D. Brainstorm ideas for an ad that you will create.

Product/Service: ______________________________

Message/Purpose: ______________________________

Slogan: ______________________________

E. **Create an ad using your ideas from (D).**

Words that I Have Learned

___

___

___

UNIT 8

Rainforest Animals

Rainforest Animals

SPIDER MONKEY

They have very long spider-like limbs. Their tails can be up to about 86 cm long. They live in the high canopy of the rainforest. They eat fruits, leaves, nuts, and occasionally, insects.

PIRANHA

They are freshwater fish. They can reach up to one foot in length. They have very sharp, interlocking teeth and powerful jaws. They are found in the rivers and streams of South America. They eat smaller fish.

POISON DART FROG

They have brightly coloured bodies which warn potential predators of their toxicity. They live near marshes, streams, and rivers. They eat insects, like termites, flies, and ants.

TOUCAN

They have compact bodies, large bills, and small wings. They make their nests in tree hollows and tree holes. They eat mostly small fruits but they occasionally eat insects.

JAGUAR

They have spotted fur and an exceptionally powerful bite. Their bodies are compact and muscular. They can be found in rainforests, swamps, and grasslands. They eat a variety of animals including deer and turtles.

ANACONDA

They can reach over nine metres in length. They can be green, yellow, or darkly spotted. They live near water and swim in streams and rivers. They hunt by waiting for prey underwater. They eat rodents, fish, birds, turtles, and even larger animals.

A. Circle the answers.

1. Which animal has a brightly coloured body?

   the poison dart frog

   the piranha

   the spider monkey

2. Which animal lives in grasslands and swamps?

   the jaguar

   the piranha

   the poison dart frog

3. Which animal lives in fresh water?

   the jaguar

   the poison dart frog

   the piranha

4. Which animal lives in the canopy of the rainforest?

   the toucan

   the poison dart frog

   the spider monkey

The heading of a diagram tells what the entire text is about. It is usually found at the top of a page. A subheading tells what a particular section is about.

B. Answer the questions.

1. What are the heading and subheadings?

   Heading: ______________________________

   Subheadings: ______________ ______________

   ______________ ______________

   ______________ ______________

2. How did the spider monkey get its name?

   ____

3. Describe the diet of the poison dart frog.

   ____

4. How does the anaconda catch its food?

   ____

C. **Look at the diagram. Colour each circle and the box connected to it the same colour. Use different colours for the four pairs. Then answer the questions.**

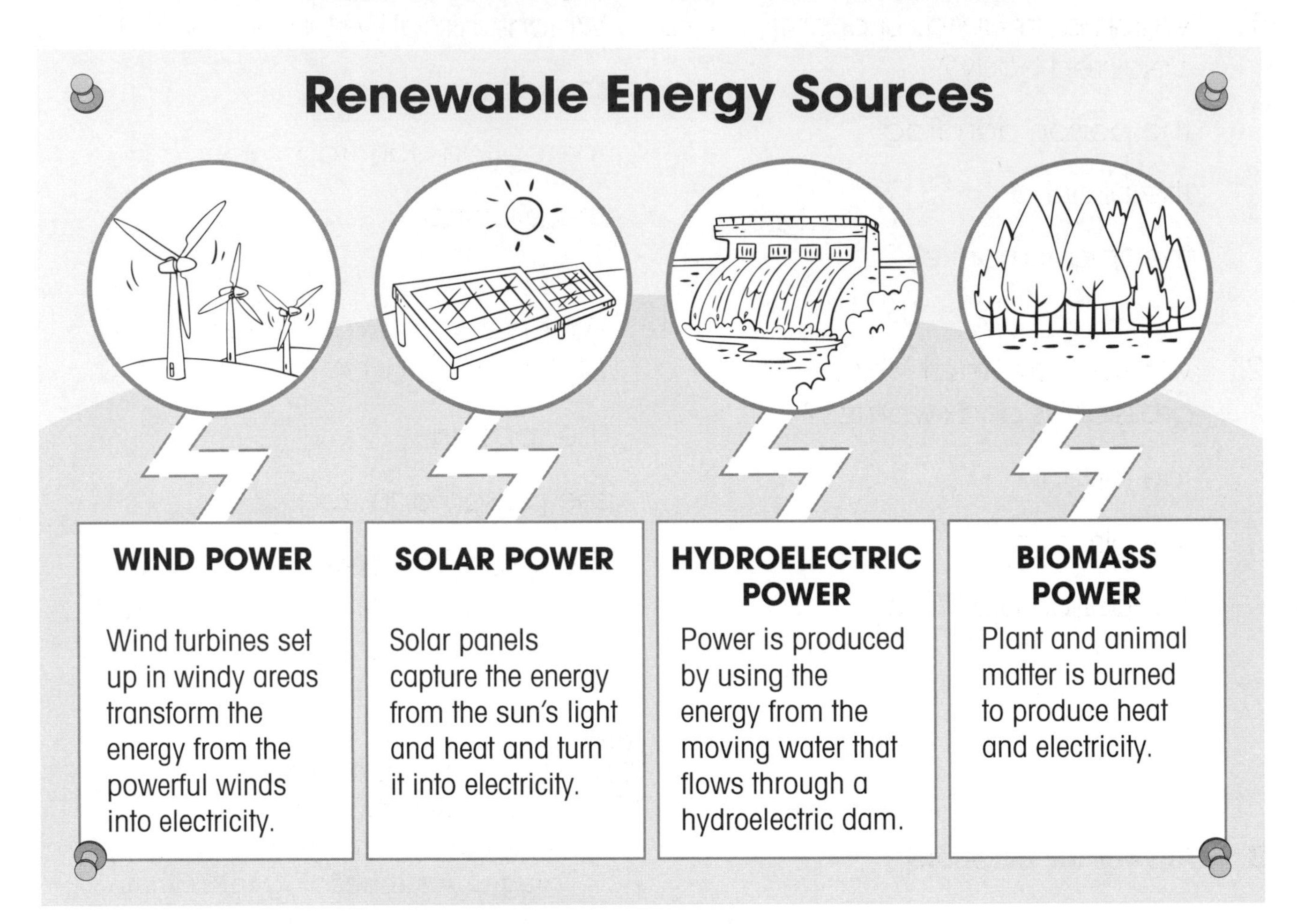

1. What is the heading of the diagram?

____

2. What are the subheadings?

____

____

3. How does the use of colour make it easier to understand this chart?

____

____

4. Why are the layout and illustrations of the text important?

____

____

D. Create your own diagram.

Words that I Have Learned

Section 4 Reading and Writing

UNIT 9

Pocahontas

Pocahontas is believed to have been born in 1596. She was the daughter of the Powhatan chief. It was not uncommon for a girl from the tribe to go by four different names. In 1607, when she was 11 or 12, Matoaka was already known by a second name, Amonute. But it is her third name, Pocahontas – meaning "playful one" – that hints at what endeared her to the strangers in her land. English colonists had moved into Powhatan territory. Needing the Powhatans for their resources and knowledge, the English wanted to build a trading relationship. They found in young Pocahontas, who was the favourite daughter of the chief, an ally in negotiations with her father. Respect, and even fondness, between Pocahontas and the English leader John Smith helped the English survive summer droughts and bad winters. At this time, Pocahontas often acted as the translator and ambassador of her tribe. Also, her bravery and cleverness helped soften the tensions that sometimes grew between the two groups.

By the time Pocahontas was a teenager, the relationship between the Powhatan and the English had broken down. Pocahontas paid the price – she was kidnapped. While her father failed to negotiate her release, Pocahontas lived among her English captors, learning their language and their religion.

Eventually, Pocahontas married an English settler named John Rolfe. At the same time, she converted to Christianity and took her fourth name: Rebecca. With their baby son Thomas in tow, the couple sailed to England. The long journey was not only to show England to Pocahontas, but to show Pocahontas to England. Funds for the trip came from a large company that was desperate for the colony in Powhatan territory to succeed. They needed more colonists, and Pocahontas was seen as an advocate for the cause.

Pocahontas was never to leave England. She became ill – possibly of pneumonia or tuberculosis – and died, still a young woman, in the country of the colonists who changed her world. She was buried at St. George's church on March 21, 1617. The memory of this courageous and brilliant woman lives to this day.

A. Circle the answers.

1. Which tribe does Pocahontas belong to?

   the English

   the Matoaka

   the Powhatan

2. What does "Pocahontas" mean?

   chief's daughter

   playful one

   ally

3. What was Pocahontas's final name?

   Rebecca

   Amonute

   Matoaka

4. Whom did Pocahontas marry?

   the English leader

   her kidnapper

   an English settler

B. Answer the questions.

1. What is the purpose of this biography of Pocahontas?

A biography is an account of a person's life.

____

____

2. How did Pocahontas help the English?

____

____

3. Why did Pocahontas live among the English when she was a teenager?

____

____

4. Why did the English want to show Pocahontas to England?

____

____

C. Research a famous person that you want to write a biography on. Fill in the information.

Biography Details Form

Name: ______________________________

Date and Place of Birth: ______________________________

Family: ______________________________

____

Main Tragedies in Life:

- ______________________________
- ______________________________
- ______________________________
- ______________________________
- ______________________________

Main Achievements in Life:

- ______________________________
- ______________________________
- ______________________________
- ______________________________
- ______________________________

Other Interesting/Important Details:

- ______________________________
- ______________________________
- ______________________________

D. **Write a biography using the information from (C). Then draw or paste a picture of the person.**

Biography of ______________________

Words that I Have Learned

UNIT 10

The Brothers Grimm

LITERARY FIGURES Chapter 12

THE BROTHERS GRIMM

Jacob and Wilhelm Grimm were born in Hanau, Germany in the late 18th century. Their father was a lawyer and Jacob and Wilhelm began to follow in their father's footsteps. But it was not to be because it was while studying law that they developed a love for folk poetry. They started researching and collecting local folk tales and putting them together. In 1812, they published the first edition of *Kinder-und Hausmärchen*, commonly referred to as *Grimm's Fairy Tales*. Many of the modern fairy tales we love today come from this anthology.

The brothers were famous for their publications of fairy tales but their lives were not always as extraordinary as their stories. The brothers went through some misfortunes. In 1796, when Jacob was only 11 years old, their father died of pneumonia. Afterwards, Jacob became responsible for providing for their mother and younger siblings. Wilhelm, on the other hand, suffered from weak health all his life. As adults, the brothers had financial difficulties and had to rely on friends and colleagues for assistance. In their later years, life became more settled and they were able to focus on composing a comprehensive German dictionary. They never completed this massive project, however, because Wilhelm died in 1859 and Jacob a few years after him.

Despite their hardships, the Brothers Grimm are now regarded as iconic literary figures, entertaining children everywhere with classic tales of princes and princesses, magic mirrors, poisoned apples, glass slippers, and gingerbread houses.

ASK YOURSELF

- What is an anthology?
- What misfortunes did the Brothers Grimm undergo?
- How are the Brothers Grimm "iconic" literary figures?

167

A. Circle the answers.

1. What were Jacob and Wilhelm famously called?

   the Grimm Brothers

   the Brothers of Grimm

   the Brothers Grimm

2. Where were the brothers born?

   in Hanau

   in Hawaii

   in Hanover

3. What was their father's profession?

   writer

   lawyer

   publisher

4. What were the brothers working on that was never completed?

   a dictionary

   an anthology

   a textbook

B. Answer the questions.

Focus questions are questions typically found at the end of the chapter in a textbook to encourage discussion and test a student's knowledge.

1. Give an example of a focus question from the textbook page.

   ____

   ____

2. How did the Brothers Grimm come up with *Kinder-und Hausmärchen*?

   ____

   ____

3. What hardship did the Brothers Grimm face as adults?

   ____

   ____

4. Why was their German dictionary never completed?

   ____

   ____

Section 4 Reading and Writing

C. Brainstorm ideas for a textbook page that you will write.

Heading: ______________________________

Subheadings: ______________________________

____

Images: ______________________________

____

Think about your topic. What are the useful points and images that you can use to make your textbook page effective?

Ideas for Body Paragraphs:

Focus Questions:

-
-
-

D. **Write a textbook page using your ideas from (C). Then draw a picture to go with it.**

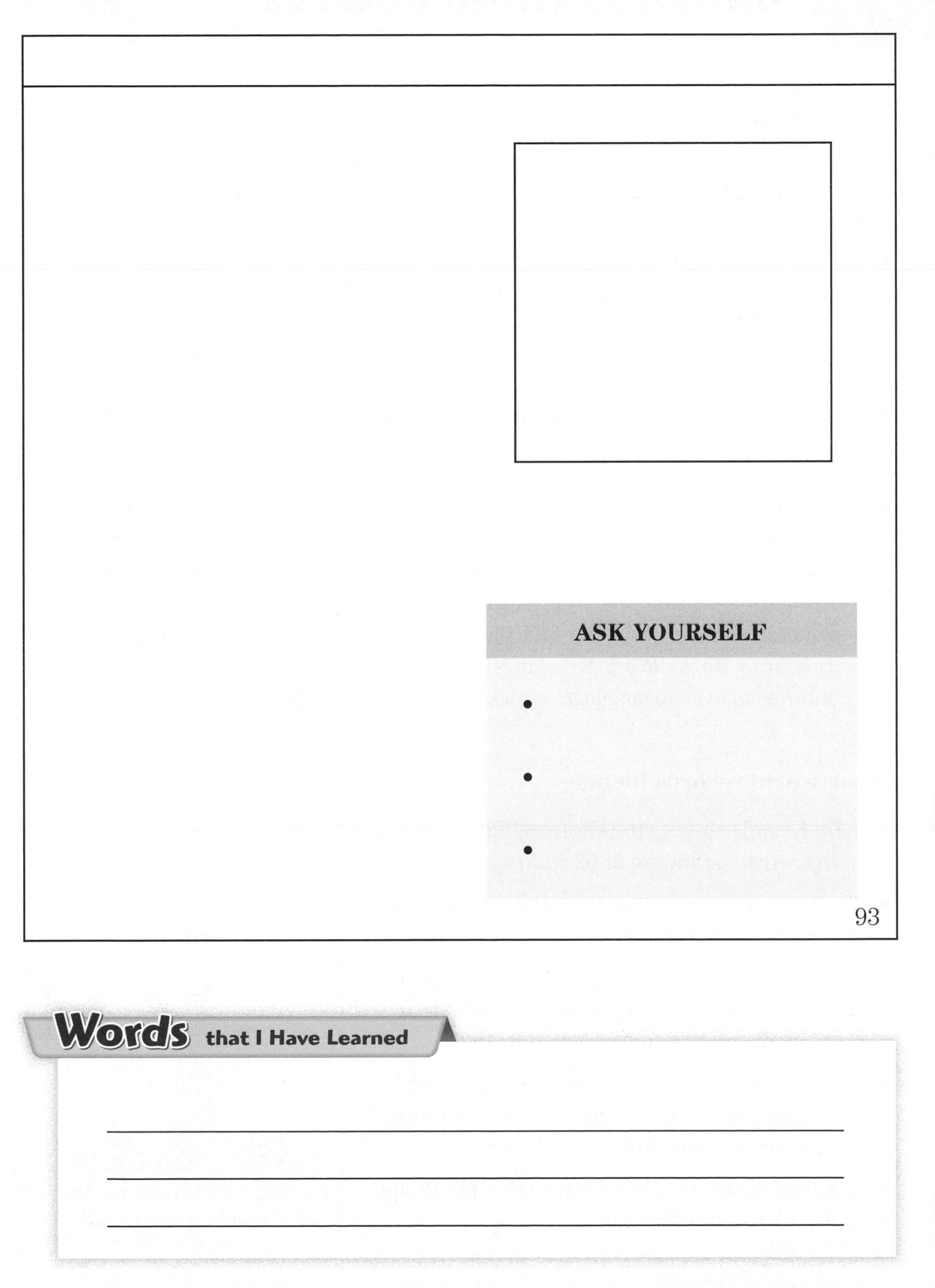

Words that I Have Learned

UNIT 11

Guinness World Records

Guinness

Guinness World Records – *The Guinness World Records* is a reference book that lists world records achieved by people and those found in nature. In the early 1950s, the managing director of the Guinness Brewery (established by Arthur Guinness in 1759), Sir Hugh Beaver, found himself involved, on more than one occasion, in arguments about trivial facts. It occurred to him that pub patrons everywhere were disputing facts on a variety of topics and that a book that could offer definitive answers to such arguments would be a useful reference. He also realized that such a book would be a great promotional idea, so he planned to publish it and make it available to pub licensees everywhere.

In 1954, Beaver approached the McWhirter brothers, who owned a fact-finding company in London, to gather facts for what became *The Guinness Book of Records*. It took over a year of painstaking research to compile and verify the information and in 1955, the first copy, a 198-page edition, was published. It became an instant bestseller and the No. 1 selling book in Britain that year. *The Guinness World Records*, as it is known today, is now sold in more than 100 countries in over 40 languages with sales of over 140 million copies.

Some world records include:

- Jyoti Kisanji Amge is the shortest living woman in the world, standing at 62.8 cm.
- The largest pizza was made in Italy with a total surface area of 1261.65 m^2.
- The oldest human to ever live was Jeanne Louise Calment of France, who was 122 years and 164 days old when she died in 1997.
- The bulldog ant in Australia is the world's most dangerous ant. It has killed at least three people since 1936 with its venomous bite.
- The Burj Khalifa in Dubai is the tallest building in the world at 828 m tall.

The Burj Khalifa has been the tallest building since 2008.

A. Circle the answers.

1. Who created *The Guinness World Records*?

   Arthur Guinness

   Jyoti Kisanji Amge

   Sir Hugh Beaver

2. Who were disputing facts on random topics?

   pub patrons

   pub owners

   pub licensees

3. When was the first *The Guinness Book of Records* published?

   in 1759

   in 1936

   in 1955

4. Where can you find the bulldog ant?

   in London

   in Italy

   in Australia

B. Answer the questions.

A caption is a brief title or explanation of a picture or an illustration.

1. What is the purpose of the caption?

   ____

   ____

2. Why did Sir Hugh Beaver think that a reference book was a good idea?

   ____

   ____

3. What happened when *The Guinness Book of Records* was published in 1955?

   ____

4. Is the bulldog ant an achievement of humans or nature?

   ____

5. What record does the Burj Khalifa make?

   ____

C. Label the encyclopedia entry. Then answer the questions.

Parts of an Encyclopedia Entry	
caption	explanation
heading	diagram
entry	label

1.

telescope

2.

telescope – A telescope is an instrument used to observe objects from far away. It is typically used by astronomers and scientists to observe and study objects in space.

3.

The first telescope was invented in 1608 by a Dutch lensmaker named Hans Lippershey. In 1609, Galileo Galilei improved upon the original telescope and built his own, and subsequently discovered the four largest moons of Jupiter (Io, Europa, Ganymede, and Callisto).

These days, there are many types of telescopes: radio telescope, X-ray telescope, refracting telescope, and reflecting telescope.

4.

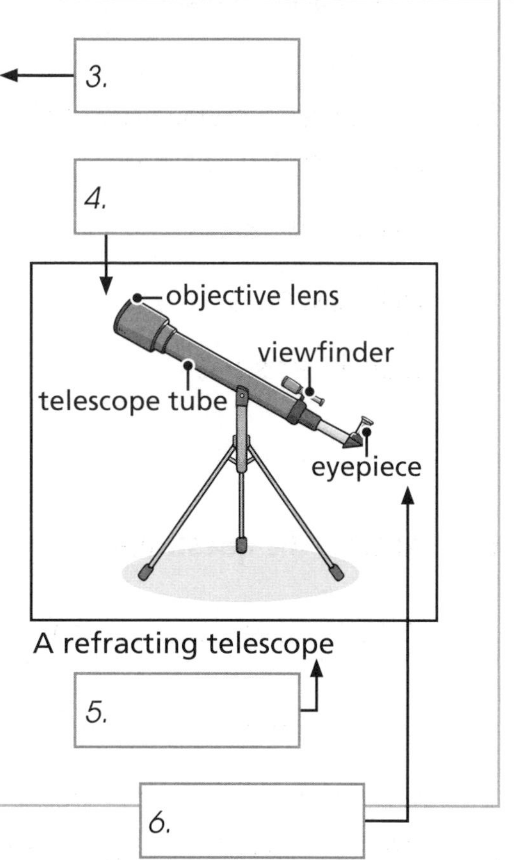

A refracting telescope

5.

6.

7. How does the diagram help readers learn more about the telescope?

____

8. What other images could have been used in this encyclopedia entry?

____

9. Research the telescope and write an additional piece of information to include in the entry.

____

____

____

D. **Write your own encyclopedia entry.**

Your entry can be about anything. Make sure to include a heading, an entry, a brief explanation, and some type of visual aid, like a chart, graph, diagram, or picture.

Words that I Have Learned

UNIT 12

C. S. Lewis's Dedication to Education

SMART DAILY **Editorial** OCTOBER 19, 2019

C. S. Lewis's Dedication to Education

C. S. Lewis's classic children's book series *The Chronicles of Narnia* has sold over 100 million copies and has been translated into 47 different languages. The series is one of the most well-known classics in children's literature. But what makes Lewis's works so important?

Lewis held many different jobs during his lifetime but they were all related to education. Fresh out of school, Lewis became a teacher of philosophy and English at the prestigious Oxford and Cambridge universities. Lewis was also drawn to the Christian religion and was determined to explain the things about religion he had thought deeply about. This included leading a club that debated religious issues, writing about spirituality, and broadcasting his views on his own radio program. Lewis had many ways of voicing his thoughts.

Lewis not only taught but continued to learn as one of the founding members of the Inklings – an informal literary discussion group that met regularly at a pub to share and critique one another's work. Over coffee and biscuits, he exchanged ideas with such writers as J. R. R. Tolkien.

If Lewis's work could be described in one word, it would be "educating". It was not enough for Lewis to think deeply; he wanted to share deeply too. He was a teacher and teaching was the thread that ran through all of Lewis's works. *The Chronicles of Narnia* are indeed a success but Lewis was more than an author. He was a teacher, even as an author. Teachers do not measure their success in how many books they sell or how much money they make. For C. S. Lewis, as with most teachers, success is seen in his students, and that is immeasurable.

A. Circle the answers.

1. What subjects did C. S. Lewis teach at Oxford and Cambridge universities?

   philosophy and religion

   English and philosophy

   religion and English

2. What did Lewis help to found?

   a book club

   a religious group

   a writers' group

3. What was Lewis's writers' group called?

   the Writelings

   the Twinklings

   the Inklings

4. Which word best describes C. S. Lewis's work?

   educating

   inspirational

   dedicated

An editorial is an article in a newspaper or magazine that expresses the opinions of the publisher or editorial staff. An opinion is one's personal belief or judgment of something or someone.

B. Answer the questions.

1. What is the writer's opinion of C. S. Lewis in this editorial?

   ____

   ____

2. How did Lewis voice his religious beliefs?

   ____

   ____

3. How did Lewis continue to learn as a member of the Inklings?

   ____

4. Why was C. S. Lewis "more than an author"?

   ____

   ____

C. Choose a type of editorial. Then brainstorm ideas for an editorial that you will write.

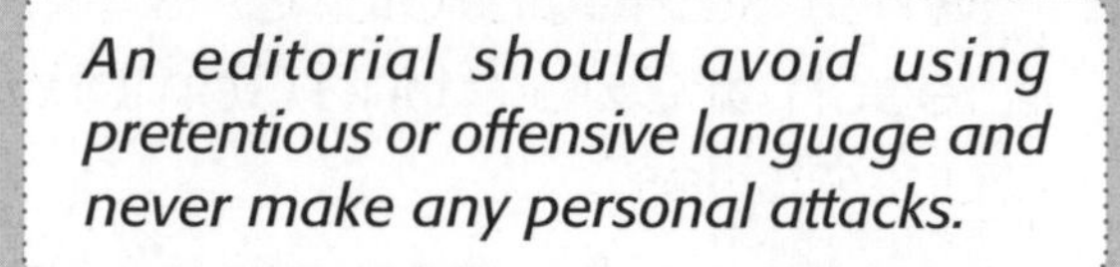

An editorial can do four things:

1. Explain – explaining an event, idea, or theory; presenting both sides and taking no side
2. Criticize – criticizing issues, problems, or news events
3. Persuade – persuading readers into taking specific action immediately
4. Praise – praising people, groups, or organizations for specific achievements

Topic: ______________________________

Opinion: ______________________________

____

Purpose: ______________________________

Facts/Supporting Evidence:

D. **Write an editorial using your ideas from (C).**

SMART DAILY **Editorial** ____________ Date

______________________________ Headline

____

Words **that I Have Learned**

____

Kelly's Blog

www.kellysblog.pop.com

KELLY'S CORNER

Home | About | Contact

Today I Tried Something New

January 5, 2019

I am not good at trying new things. I usually play the same games after school, go to the same mall on the weekends, and eat the same food every day. It's easy to fall into a rut and never challenge yourself to be adventurous.

Well, today I tried something new. I challenged myself to get out of my comfort zone and I ended up singing karaoke in front of an audience at my friend's birthday party! We are all used to humming a tune to ourselves, or singing in the shower, but it takes a lot of nerve to stand on a stage and let other people judge you.

I'm usually shy and anxious about performing for a group – even doing presentations in class makes me nervous. And though I was hesitant to get up on that stage, I forced myself to, and once I started singing, I couldn't stop! I ended up having so much fun and the crowd gave me an eager round of applause. I felt great!

I've been trying to do something new every week to break the dullness of my routine. Life can get boring if you never try anything new. So, whether it is camping in your backyard, trying a food you've never tried before, or waking up an hour earlier than usual, talk yourself into doing one new thing every week!

Tags: #lifestyle #personal 2 COMMENTS

My name is Kelly Kahn and I love to read, write, and have a good time!

BLOG ARCHIVE

- 2019 (1)
  - January (1)
    - Today I Tried Something New
- 2018 (10)

Copyright@blogs.pop.com 2019 | Terms of Use

A. Circle the answers.

1. What is the blogger not good at doing?

   falling into a rut

   trying new things

   doing the same things

2. Where did the blogger sing karaoke?

   at her friend's birthday party

   at her birthday party

   at her sister's birthday party

3. How does the blogger feel when performing for a group?

   excited

   thrilled

   anxious

4. How often does the blogger try to do something new?

   every day

   every week

   every month

B. Answer the questions.

A blog is an online informational diary or journal where the blogger (the writer) shares his or her personal experiences, photographs, knowledge, insights, and views about subjects on a regular basis.

1. What is this blog entry about?

   ____

   ____

2. What are the things the blogger usually does?

   ____

   ____

3. Why is it important to try something new?

   ____

   ____

4. What are some of the blogger's suggestions of new things to try?

   ____

   ____

C. **Read "Today I Tried Something New" again. Then fill in the information and check the features of the blog.**

1. **Heading**

2. **Post Title**

3. **Name of Blogger**

4. **Post Date**

5. What other features does the blog have?

- ◯ menu/navigation bar
- ◯ blog posts ordered from last to first
- ◯ footer
- ◯ attention-grabbing title
- ◯ subheadings
- ◯ contact information
- ◯ tags
- ◯ comment section
- ◯ sidebar with social profile
- ◯ site map
- ◯ image(s)
- ◯ terms of use and copyright section

D. **Fill in the mind map with ideas for a blog post that you will create.**

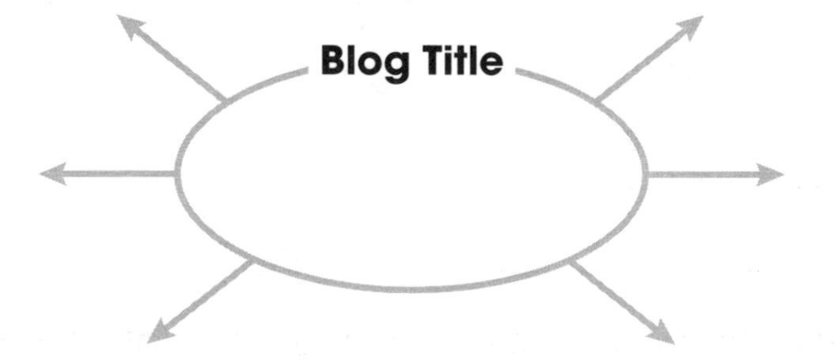

E. **Create a blog post using your ideas from (D). Remember to include as many features of a blog as possible.**

Words that I Have Learned

UNIT 14

All about Good Food!

Hey listeners! Do you want to live better? Do you want to live longer? Well, Health Canada has made a food guide just for you to help you live the healthy life you've always wanted.

The food guide is easy and straightforward. It tells you about the different food groups you should choose from on a daily basis and even tells you how much of them to eat! It also suggests how active you need to be to avoid the risk of getting serious illnesses like diabetes, osteoporosis, heart disease, and certain types of cancer.

The food guide recommends we eat at least one dark green vegetable and one orange vegetable a day. But remember, it's best to eat the veggies in their most natural state. Health Canada recommends that we consume different types of grains, like oats, barley, and brown rice. Dairy products, like milk, cheese, and yogourt, are also important. Meats or alternatives that contain protein, like beans, lentils, and fish, should be consumed regularly as well.

One last thing – remember to make mealtime fun! You can do this by eating with your family. It's a great way to talk about one another's day over a delicious and healthful meal. Help cook, set the table, and try different recipes! Eating can be fun and interesting.

Eating healthfully and being active have many benefits and can be enjoyable too! It is important to take the time to make sure we are taking care of ourselves and those around us.

A. Circle the answers.

1. What serious illness can we avoid by being active?

   heart disease

   asthma

   chicken pox

2. What colours of vegetables should we consume each day?

   red and orange

   yellow and green

   green and orange

3. What do beans, lentils, and fish contain?

   grain

   protein

   meat

4. What is one way of making mealtime fun?

   eating with your family

   eating while watching TV

   eating at a restaurant

In marketing, CTA stands for "Call to Action" and it is what a company wants its audience to do after listening to or viewing their ad.

B. Answer the questions.

1. Is the CTA compelling and relevant in this radio commercial? Explain.

   ____

   ____

2. How is the food guide "easy and straightforward"?

   ____

   ____

   ____

3. What does Health Canada recommend we consume?

   ____

   ____

   ____

Section 4 Reading and Writing

C. Read the radio commercial script. Then answer the questions.

Everyone loves a treat so come and enjoy what everybody else is! Enjoy warm, homemade doughnuts by Damien's Dangerously Delish Doughnuts. With over 50 different flavours, we have a doughnut that's good for every mood – whether it's cinnamon to keep you cozy on a chilly night or mint to refresh you on a sunny summer day. Drop by one of our 30 locations in Toronto and pick up some sweet treats. Damien's Dangerously Delish Doughnuts are to die for!

1. What is the company's name?

____

2. What are they advertising?

____

3. Is the commercial compelling? Why or why not?

____

D. Brainstorm ideas for a radio commercial that you will write.

Company Name	**Offer**
CTA	**Audience and How You Will Persuade Them**

E. **Write a script for a radio commercial using your ideas from (D).**

One of the most important elements of a radio commercial is its catchiness. A radio commercial has to capture the listener's attention. It has to have a straightforward and clear message to make it effective.

Radio Commercial Script

Words that I Have Learned

A. Circle the answers.

1. Which literary device is used to make a comparison?

   personification

   alliteration

   metaphor

2. Legends are loosely based on ______ .

   real people, events, or places

   imaginary people, events, or places

   mythical people, events, or places

3. What is a group of lines in a poem called?

   a meter

   a stanza

   a verse

4. In ______ , the first letter of each line spells a word or phrase when it is read downward.

   an acrostic poem

   a haiku

   a limerick

5. Which of the following is not a main element of a short story?

   theme

   stanza

   point of view

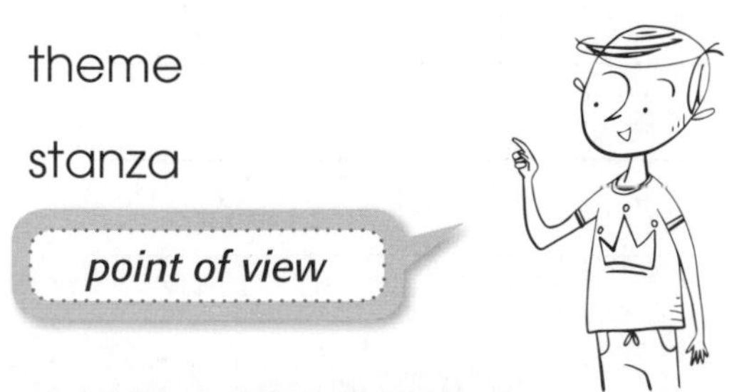

6. What is the villain of a short story called?

   the opponent

   the protagonist

   the antagonist

7. Which of the following is a common element found in fantasy stories?

   advanced technology

   the supernatural

   mystery

8. A fantasy story includes ______ .

   magical characters and creatures

   aliens, machines, and robots

   real people and places

9. What type of narrative is used to teach moral lessons?

   a myth

   an epic

   an anecdote

10. What are the common types of characters found in a myth?

    fairies and elves

    gods and goddesses

    ghosts and ghouls

11. Which one contains panels?

a graphic novel

an encyclopedia entry

a short story

12. What is the purpose of an ad?

to explain

to persuade

to describe

13. Which is used in a diagram to tell what a section is about?

a heading

a caption

a subheading

14. A diagram includes ______ .

a heading, subheadings, and images

a heading, subheadings, and dialogue

a heading, subheadings, and tags

15. An account of someone's life written by another person is called ______ .

a biography

an autobiography

an anthology

16. In which type of text are focus questions found?

a diagram

an editorial

a textbook

17. Which of the following is not a purpose of an editorial?

to criticize

to sell

to explain

18. Which of the following is a common feature of a blog?

a sidebar with a social profile

a site map

subheadings

19. What does CTA stand for in marketing?

Call to Attention

Call to Action

Call to Activity

20. One of the most important elements of a radio commercial is its ______ .

catchiness

descriptiveness

ambiguity

B. **Read the travel blog. Then check the true statements.**

LUNA'S TRAVELS

Home | About | Contact

France – Day 3: The Palace of Versailles

Tuesday, August 27, 2019

I woke up today, on my third day in Paris, France, not knowing I would end up at the lavish Palace of Versailles. I woke up early enough that I arrived before the gold-leafed Royal Gate opened at 9 a.m. The 45-minute train ride southwest to Versailles went by pleasantly fast, though it was more crowded than I thought it would be.

Once there, I overheard a tour guide saying that the 700-room palace was originally built in 1624 as a hunting lodge for King Louis XIII, but was transformed over many decades into an elaborate palace for his son, Louis XIV. I couldn't help but be blown away by the extravagance!

There was a lot to take in, including the expansive gardens, fountains, and the trianons (which I learned are elegant villa-like structures). I was instantly drawn to the Marble Court – a terrace covered in a bold black and white checkered marble floor. I could have spent all day looking at the dozens of marble busts that overlooked the space!

Before lunch, I was able to walk through the Hall of Mirrors – perhaps my favourite place I visited within the palace. It has 17 broad arcaded mirrors opposite 17 large windows overlooking the gardens, and there are beautiful glass chandeliers reflecting light off the mirrored surfaces. The whole space dazzled!

Not wanting to travel back into the city after the evening fountain show, I opted to stay in Versailles, right outside the gates at the Waldorf Astoria Trianon. Visiting the Palace of Versailles was unplanned, but it is a visit I will not soon forget!

My name is Luna Lloyd. I'm a photographer, traveller, and blogger who has visited 24 countries around the world. Welcome to my blog!

BLOG ARCHIVE

- 2019 (6)
  - August (4)
    - France – Day 3: The Palace of Versailles
    - France – Day 2: Paris Love
    - France – Day 1: I'm here!
    - I'm going to France!
  - July (1)
  - June (1)
- 2018 (5)

Tags: #travels #places #lifestyle 8 Comments

Copyright@blogs.pop.com 2019 | Terms of Use

1. Luna visited the Palace of Versailles on her third day in France. ◯

2. Luna arrived at the Royal Gate after 9 a.m. ◯

3. It took Luna 45 minutes to travel by plane from Paris to Versailles. ◯

4. Versailles is located southwest of Paris. ◯

5. The Palace of Versailles has 700 rooms. ◯

6. Trianons are elegant villa-like structures. ◯

7. The Marble Court is a terrace covered in a blue and white checkered marble floor. ◯

C. Answer the questions.

1. List two features of a travel blog. Explain the purpose of each.

___

___

2. What is the purpose of keeping a detailed blog of one's travels?

___

___

3. Identify and describe the writer's favourite place in the palace.

___

___

___

4. What information is given about the writer of the blog in the sidebar?

___

___

D. Check the features of an ad. Then complete the ad by writing information you have learned about the Palace of Versailles.

VERSAILLES BY NIGHT

Experience the magic of a moonlit Versailles!

The Palace of Versailles...

All Tour Packages Include:

- skip-the-line entrance
- hotel pickup and roundtrip transport
- a 3-hour guided tour across the grounds

Visit www.versaillesbynight.pop.com for more information.

E. **Create a textbook page about the Palace of Versailles.**

PLACES Chapter 15

THE PALACE OF VERSAILLES

Figure 15.1 The Palace of Versailles

ASK YOURSELF

•

•

•

174

1.1 The Monarch Butterfly

The butterfly has long been a symbol of beauty. It has been around for nearly 50 million years. There are about 19 000 known species of butterflies. The Monarch butterfly is a milkweed butterfly. It is a member of Lepidoptera, the fourth largest order of insects. The Monarch is easily recognized by its reddish-brown wings, spotted with white dots and framed by a black border. It is commonly found in North America.

The metamorphosis and migration of the Monarch butterfly are two phenomena that make this insect one of the most interesting of all living creatures. In the caterpillar stage, the Monarch feeds on milkweed leaves and grows. It outgrows and sheds its skin a few times until it is about two inches in length. Then it hangs upside down, sheds its skin for the last time, and enters the pupa stage. In the pupa stage, the caterpillar is encased in a jade green shell where it undergoes great transformation. After about two weeks, this hard capsule cracks open and a beautiful, fully-grown adult butterfly emerges.

Although Monarchs live in the temperate climates of North America, they cannot endure the cold temperature consistent with seasonal changes. When the days get shorter and the air gets cooler, the Monarch instinctively prepares to migrate to a warmer climate. What is truly remarkable is the distance that these tiny, apparently fragile creatures can travel. Although there is a great deal yet to be learned about this mysterious migratory flight, it is known that the Monarch butterfly will travel up to 3000 kilometres one way to reach its winter roosts. Since the Monarch does not fly at night, it covers up to 130 km in a day. Favourite southern locations for the Monarch include Florida, California, and central Mexico.

1.2

1. Which one is true about the Monarch butterfly?
   A. It's a milkweed butterfly.
   B. It's the fourth largest insect.

2. At what stage does the Monarch butterfly feed on milkweed leaves?
   A. the pupa stage
   B. the caterpillar stage

3. Why do Monarch butterflies migrate?
   A. They cannot withstand the cold weather.
   B. It is still a mystery.

4. What is remarkable about the Monarch butterfly's migratory flight?
   A. the distance they travel
   B. the speed in which they travel

2.1 Leonardo da Vinci – Artist and Visionary

Leonardo da Vinci is one of the most famous artists of all time. Immediately coming to mind at the mention of his name are the paintings of The Last Supper, John the Baptist, and the most renowned painting in the world, The Mona Lisa. However, da Vinci was not just a great painter. He was also a visionary who drew sketches and plans for some of the great inventions of the future.

Concerned with a war raging with Venice, da Vinci designed a chariot with spear-like protrusions on each side to strike the enemy. He also sketched a drawing of an armoured car complete with wheels and a crank mechanism, arguably the first depiction of the modern-day tank.

In da Vinci's time, Milan was filthy and overcome by a devastating plague. Da Vinci, disgusted with the conditions, designed a city with an elaborate sewage system complete with drainage. The lower level was also a place where horse stables could be housed. Da Vinci actually installed a similar design to work in Sforza Castle in Milan.

One of da Vinci's most interesting ideas was the design of a flying machine resembling a helicopter. First he designed a set of wings like those of a bird which could be attached to a person's arms. Then he planned a machine that would feature two sets of wings attached to a long post propelled by a person sitting below pedalling. Once again, da Vinci was ahead of his time.

Da Vinci had dreamed of the possibility of humans working underwater. He designed a metal diving suit with an air bag attached. Protruding from the air bag was a tube that could be placed in the mouth, allowing the person to breathe. He also designed web-like attachments for the feet to aid propulsion underwater and a waistband filled with air to keep a person afloat.

Da Vinci may be thought of as a man born beyond his time.

2.2

1. Why is Leonardo da Vinci called a visionary?
   A. He made predictions of the future.
   B. He made sketches and plans for future inventions.

2. What did da Vinci design for the war with Venice?
   A. a chariot with spears
   B. a tank

3. What does da Vinci's flying machine look like?
   A. a helicopter
   B. the wings of a bird

4. What was attached to da Vinci's metal diving suit?
   A. an air bag
   B. web-like attachments for the feet

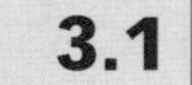

3.1 English – the Language of the World

Today, it is estimated that English is spoken by over one billion people (1/7 of the world's population) with approximately half of them having English as their mother tongue. Only Mandarin surpasses English in individual use, but no language matches English in distribution. The rise of the English language to dominance is a remarkable story. When the Roman army, led by Julius Caesar, landed in England two thousand years ago, there was no such thing as the English language. But a thousand years later, English was the native language of over six million British people. English was then spread globally to all corners of the world by military personnel, travellers, the English, Irish, Scots, and Americans who represented business and political expansion.

There is an estimate of over 6800 languages in existence in the world today, and English has by far the most extensive vocabulary. The Oxford Dictionary lists over half a million words. There is another half million of technical and scientific terms which are not included in the dictionary but are widely used. By comparison, the German language has roughly 185 000 words, while French uses approximately 100 000. English is now the language of business with over 80% of the world's telecommunications, faxes, and Internet correspondences written in English.

The most significant development of the last 100 years is the use of English as a second language by over half a billion people in countries such as India and the Netherlands. Political announcements and communications with the rest of the world promoting trade are often made in English, creating a link between non-English speaking countries and the Western world.

The desire for the world's population to learn English has spawned numerous educational agencies that arrange for English language classes in Asian countries such as China, Japan, and Korea. With the dominance of English and six billion people worldwide as potential speakers of the language, the task of providing this education is daunting.

3.2

1. When did the English language come into existence?
   A. about a thousand years ago
   B. about two thousand years ago

2. Who first used English?
   A. the Americans
   B. the British

3. Which language has a more extensive vocabulary?
   A. English
   B. German

4. What was the most significant development of English in the last century?
   A. the use of English in Asian countries
   B. the use of English as a second language by over half a billion people

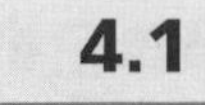

The Great Pyramid of Ancient Egypt

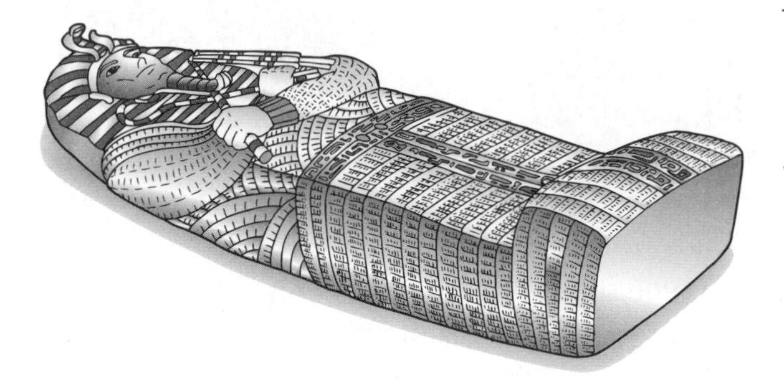

The Great Pyramid of ancient Egypt has been a mystery for centuries. It was constructed under the reign of the pharaoh Khufu.

When Khufu ascended to the throne, he declared himself to be the manifestation of both the gods, Horus and Ra. A claim like this had never been made before. The Egyptians were overwhelmed and they declared Khufu the greatest pharaoh of all time.

Khufu lived luxuriously, sparing no expense in entertaining important guests and spoiling them with lavish gifts of gold, precious jewels, and silks. Khufu knew that the wonderfully pleasurable life he was leading would not last forever and that he must prepare for the afterlife with the gods. Since he had proclaimed himself the greatest pharaoh, he was compelled to back up his claim by constructing the greatest pyramid of all time.

The location of this great pyramid was important. It had to be in the Western Desert in a location close to the Land of the Dead, where the Egyptians believed they could carry on with the rest of their existence after death, yet in a spot unique to him. He chose the Giza Plateau. It was the perfect location. The firmness of the land provided a perfect foundation for the structure and this location happened to rise high above the landscape, creating a monumental presence for his pyramid. Over 35 000 labourers were drawn from nearby farms to work full time on this project. It is believed that the construction of the Great Pyramid took many years.

Khufu died in 2566 BCE. He was mummified, a process lasting 65 days, and lowered into the sarcophagus inside the pyramid. The work of devoted priests and labourers was not yet over as they then bore the responsibility of protecting the tomb and organizing ceremonies to honour the greatest pharaoh of all time.

4.2

1. Why was Khufu declared the greatest pharaoh?
   A. He built the Great Pyramid.
   B. He claimed he was the manifestation of the gods, Horus and Ra.

2. Where did the Egyptians believe they could continue their existence after death?
   A. the Giza Plateau
   B. the Land of the Dead

3. Why did Khufu choose the Giza Plateau for his pyramid?
   A. It was a place with a beautiful landscape.
   B. It rose high above the landscape.

4. How long did it take to mummify Khufu?
   A. 35 days
   B. 65 days

5.1 Thomas Edison – the Greatest Inventor in History

With more than 1000 patented discoveries to his credit, Thomas Edison was one of the greatest scientists who profoundly shaped modern technology. However, when Edison was young, no one expected him to excel in life.

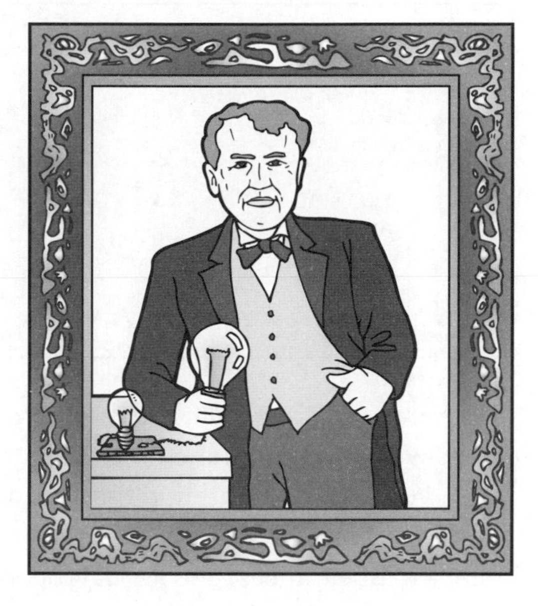

When he was seven, Edison's family moved from Ohio to Michigan in the United States after his father landed a carpentry job at a military post. Edison entered school in Port Huron but he did not do well as a student.

Because of hearing problems, he had difficulty following the lessons and often played truant. However, Edison did not while away his time. Instead, he used the time to read books and set up a laboratory in the basement of his home. But the smell from his laboratory was often so strong that his mother had to stop him from carrying out any more experiments at home.

At the age of 12, Edison got a job as a train boy on the Grand Trunk Railway. There, he made use of an abandoned freight car as his laboratory. He even learned how to use the telegraph and later became a roving telegrapher in the Midwest, New England, the South of the United States, and Canada. During that time, he successfully developed a device that could transmit messages automatically. By 1869, Edison's inventions in telegraphy were widely adopted, which made him decide to leave the job and become a full-time inventor. Edison's most well-known inventions include the electric light bulb, the carbon-button transmitter used in telephone speakers and microphones, and the phonograph. In explaining how he could come up with so many inventions, Edison said, "Genius is one percent inspiration and ninety-nine percent perspiration."

Thomas Edison died at the age of 84 on October 18, 1931. At the time of his death, he was still doing experiments in his laboratory in West Orange, New Jersey. He clearly enjoyed his work as an inventor and lived life to its fullest.

5.2

1. What was Thomas Edison's father?
   A. a soldier
   B. a carpenter
2. Why didn't Edison do well at school?
   A. He had hearing problems.
   B. He skipped school too often.
3. What did Edison do right before he became a full-time inventor?
   A. He was a roving telegrapher.
   B. He was a train boy.
4. What are two of Edison's inventions?
   A. the freight car and the telegraph
   B. the phonograph and the light bulb

R1.1 The Mysterious Bermuda Triangle

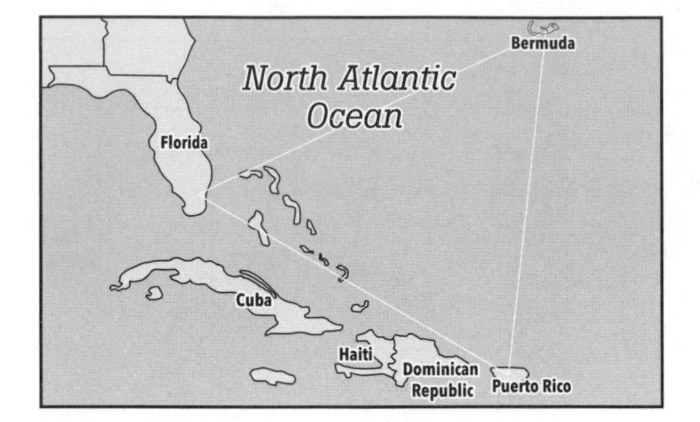

The names "Bermuda Triangle" or "Devil's Triangle", as it is referred to by some, are unofficial titles for the triangular area of the Atlantic between Miami, Florida; Bermuda; and San Juan, Puerto Rico. The area covers over a million square kilometres of ocean and is notorious for the unexplained disappearances of numerous ships, small craft, and airplanes. The most notable is the mysterious vanishing of the entire US Navy flight squadron, Flight 19.

There are two schools of thought on these disappearances. One is the popular belief that supernatural forces were at play. Some theorize that the devil was doing his handiwork. Some theorize that aliens sucked up both the craft and the occupants through a vacuum-like funnel hurling them into space and whisking them away to another planet. One thing is certain: there were very strange forces at work during these disappearances, and logical theories and explanations have fallen short of satisfying the skeptics.

A more rational way of thinking is to consider the many natural explanations. This part of the Atlantic is subject to sudden storms. The Gulf Stream, which flows through this part of the Atlantic, can swiftly erase evidence of disasters at sea. The ocean floor in this area is a mixture of shoals and deep trenches, creating unpredictable marine conditions. In addition to environmental factors is the concept of human error. People travel in this area in craft that are too small to withstand the conditions, and without the experience to respond adequately when conditions change.

The US Coast Guard prefers to dispel any notion of supernatural or extraterrestrial forces at play. It prefers to adopt the rational viewpoint that human error, natural forces, and coincidence are factors responsible for these unsolved disasters. However, the mysterious disappearances of Flight 19 with its crew of 14 and the Martin Mariner flying boat with its crew of 13, which was sent out to search for Flight 19, strongly suggest that there was more than nature at work on that fateful December day in 1945.

R1.2

1. What is another name for the Bermuda Triangle?
   A. the Bermuda's Devil
   B. the Devil's Triangle

2. What is the Bermuda Triangle notable for?
   A. the mysterious disappearances of cars and trains
   B. the mysterious disappearances of ships and aircraft

3. What is one of the rational explanations for the disappearances?
   A. Natural forces were at play.
   B. Supernatural forces were at play.

4. How many people were on Flight 19 when it disappeared?
   A. 14
   B. 13

Answers

Answers

Section 1

1 The Monarch Butterfly

A. 1. C
   2. B
   3. B
   4. D

B. 1. A
   2. B
   3. A
   4. A

C. 1. T
   2. T
   3. F
   4. F
   5. F
   6. T
   7. T

D. 1. The great mystery surrounding the Monarch butterfly is their migratory flight.
   2. In the caterpillar stage, the Monarch feeds on milkweed leaves and grows. It outgrows and sheds its skin a few times. Then, it hangs upside down, sheds its skin for the last time, and enters the pupa stage. In the pupa stage, the caterpillar is encased in a chrysalis, which cracks open to reveal the newly transformed butterfly.
   3. (Individual answer)

E. (Individual summary)

2 Leonardo da Vinci – Artist and Visionary

A. 1. D
   2. D
   3. B
   4. A

B. 1. B
   2. A
   3. A
   4. A

C. 1. armoured car
   2. drainage
   3. Sforza Castle
   4. propulsion
   5. waistband

D. 1. Da Vinci designed a flying machine that resembled a helicopter. First, he designed a set of wings that attached to a person's arms. Then he planned a machine that would feature two sets of wings attached to a long post propelled by a person sitting below pedaling.
   2. (Suggested answer)
      People say da Vinci was "ahead of his time" because he drew sketches and plans for inventions that would be made in the future.
   3. (Individual answer)

E. (Individual summary)

3 English – the Language of the World

A. 1. A
   2. C
   3. B
   4. D

B. 1. A
   2. B
   3. A
   4. B

C. 1. T
   2. F
   3. T
   4. T
   5. T
   6. F

D. 1. The English language was spread all over the world by military personnel, travellers, and the English, Irish, Scots, and Americans who represented business and political expansion.
2. There is a surge in the need to speak English all over the world because English is now the language of business with over 80% of the world's telecommunications, faxes, and Internet correspondences written in English.
3. (Suggested answer)
The advantage of having most of the world speak English is that people all over the world can communicate easily with one another as they can speak the same language.

E. (Individual summary)

4 The Great Pyramid of Ancient Egypt

A. 1. A
2. C
3. B
4. B

B. 1. B
2. B
3. B
4. B

C. 1. labourers
2. mummified
3. sarcophagus
4. landscape
5. afterlife
6. foundation

D. 1. Khufu wanted to build the Great Pyramid because he had proclaimed himself the greatest pharaoh and was compelled to back up his claim by constructing the greatest pyramid of all time.
2. Khufu spared no expense in entertaining important guests and spoiled them with lavish gifts of gold, precious jewels, and silks.
3. After Khufu died, the priests were responsible for protecting the tomb and organizing ceremonies to honour him.

E. (Individual summary)

5 Thomas Edison – the Greatest Inventor in History

A. 1. B
2. D
3. A
4. A

B. 1. B
2. A
3. A
4. B

C. 1. F
2. T
3. T
4. T
5. F
6. T
7. F

D. 1. They moved to Michigan because Edison's father had landed a carpentry job at a military post.
2. He did not while away his time when he was not in school. He used the time to read books and set up a laboratory in the basement of his home.
3. (Suggested answer)
Edison meant that only a small percentage of genius comes from the thinking of ideas, while the vast majority comes from the hard work and perseverance required to make those ideas a reality.

E. (Individual summary)

Review 1

A. 1. Bermuda, Florida, Puerto Rico
2. over 1 million
3. Flight 19
4. two
5. sudden storms
6. the Gulf Stream
7. shoals and deep trenches
8. human error
9. 13
10. in December 1945

B. 1. B
2. B
3. A
4. A

C.

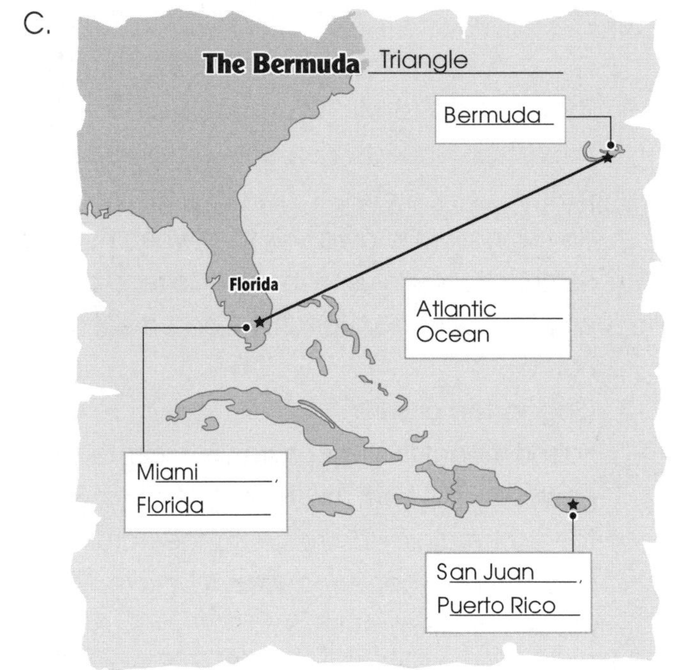

D. 1. S
2. R
3. R
4. S
5. R
6. R

E. 1. The most notable Bermuda Triangle disappearance is the vanishing of the US Navy flight squadron, Flight 19.
2. People travel in this area in craft that are too small to withstand the conditions.
3. The disappearances of Flight 19 and the Martin Mariner suggest that there were more than natural forces at work.

F. 1945
EVENT: Navy ; Flight 19 ; Devil's Triangle
DETAILS: Atlantic ; Gulf Stream ; evidence ; supernatural ; extraterrestrial ; marine conditions ; 14

G. 1. This part of the Atlantic is subject to sudden storms. The Gulf Stream can swiftly erase evidence of disasters at sea. Also, the ocean floor is a mixture of shoals and deep trenches, creating unpredictable marine conditions.
2. The US Coast Guard prefers to dispel any notion of supernatural or extraterrestrial forces at play. It prefers to adopt the rational viewpoint that human error, natural forces, and coincidence are factors responsible for the unsolved disappearances.

H. (Individual summary)

1 Parts of Speech

A. 1. Beauty ; eye ; beholder
   2. teacher ; poem ; friendship
   3. place
   4. house ; storm
   5. restaurant ; food

B. 1. reported
   2. exists
   3. surfaced
   4. revealed
   5. caused
   6. hope

C. It is difficult to argue that hockey is not the national passion of Canadians. Canada, with its frigid weather in the winter, is suitable for playing hockey. As early as 1870, British soldiers stationed in Halifax started playing hockey on frozen ponds around the city. In 1892, Lord Stanley, the Governor General of Canada, donated a silver bowl to be awarded to the best amateur team. That was the origin of the Stanley Cup.

D. (Suggested answers)
   1. Carmen quickly finished all the pasta.
   2. They went down the steep slope carefully.
   3. He was not good at swimming so he eagerly signed up for a swimming course.
   4. He nodded knowingly and started figuring out how to settle the matter effectively.

E. " (What) / **I** on earth is the gossip about?" wondered Ted. At first, (he) / **they** thought that (he) / **it** was the one his neighbours were talking about but soon realized that (they) / **it** were not talking about (him) / **it** . **She** / (He) was just being too sensitive and had almost made a fool of **itself** / (himself) . Luckily, Ted's sister did not know about (this) / **those** or (she) / **they** would tell their parents. Ted promised **herself** / (himself) never to eavesdrop on others' conversations again.

F. Joanne Kathleen Rowling, author ~~with~~ of the immensely popular Harry Potter series, went ~~through~~ from ordinary existence [to] stardom virtually overnight. The fame bestowed [upon] her was [beyond] her wildest dreams. As a single parent, [with] little money, Joanne often headed [to] a café ~~for~~ to write [about] the wizarding world [of] magic. This imaginative series has now sold [over] 450 million copies and has been adapted ~~with~~ into a blockbuster film franchise. Her success shows that you can achieve anything if you put your mind ~~of~~ to it.

G. 1. unless
   2. if
   3. although ; and
   4. or ; but
   5. Yuck
   6. Hurray
   7. Oops
   8. Look out

2 Personal, Indefinite, and Relative Pronouns

A. 1. She had a bad dream.
   2. We sit beside each other in class.
   3. They joined the chess club yesterday.
   4. It let out a loud wail as the mother gave birth.
   5. He always helps wash the dishes after dinner.
   6. You and he should watch the new horror movie.
   7. We had better clean up this mess before your parents come home.

B. 1. her
   2. him
   3. them
   4. them
   5. us

C. 1. I
2. me
3. us
4. They
5. her ; She
6. he
7. us ; He

D. 1. anybody
2. Several
3. some
4. All
5. None
6. Both
7. anything
8. Each
9. No one
10. everyone

E. 1. that
2. whom
3. whose
4. whichever
5. whomever
6. Whoever

3 Verb Tenses

A. 1. s
2.
3. s
4. s
5. s ; es
6.
7. s ; s
8. es
9.
10. s
11. es

B. 1. finished
2. continued
3. escaped
4. existed
5. polished
6. posted
7. pointed
8. planted
9. dined
10. coughed
11. advised

C. 1. will meet
2. will last
3. will name
4. will practise
5. will rain
6. will help
7. will create
8. will write
9. will have
10. will visit

D. 1. keeps
2. brings
3. drives
4. slept
5. paid
6. blew
7. will leave
8. will begin
9. will shrink

4 Progressive Tenses

A. 1. ✔
2. ✔
3.
4. ✔
5. ✔
6. ✔
7.
8.
9. ✔

Rewritten Sentences in the Present Progressive Tense:
3. Jade is visiting the zoo with her friends.
7. The chefs are making delicious desserts.
8. I am not attending the ceremony.

B. 1. was greeting
2. were playing
3. was informing
4. was eating
5. was not sleeping
6. was not raining
7. was practising
8. Was ; doing
9. was studying
10. were visiting

C. 1. Carly will be memorizing her lines for the play tomorrow morning.
2. My dad will be building the tree house this weekend.
3. Jess and Sam will not be working on the project tomorrow.
4. I will not be canoeing at the Port Perry Marina next Saturday.
5. Will she be cooking pasta for dinner this Friday?
6. Will the children be playing basketball next summer?

D. 1. Will Matias be coming
2. is wearing
3. was performing
4. was not listening
5. Was Justine painting
6. was washing
7. will be flying
8. was jogging
9. is waiting
10. was driving

5 Verbals

A. 1. swimming 2. cooling
3. to see 4. laughing
5. cooking 6. To settle down
7. jogging 8. crossing
9. driving 10. to leave
11. devoted

Gerund: swimming, cooking, jogging, driving
Participle: cooling, laughing, crossing, devoted
Infinitive: to see, To settle down, to leave

B. 1. Skydiving 2. Dreaming
3. shopping 4. dancing
5. Hiking 6. snowboarding
7. Counting 8. canoeing
9. Leading 10. volunteering
11. Smiling 12. Resting

C. 1. G 2. P
3. P 4. G
5. G 6. G
7. P 8. P

D. 1. stargazing 2. hiking
3. Baking 4. to read
5. lost 6. Daydreaming
7. to decorate 8. to survive

E. (Individual writing)

6 Phrases

A. 1. Eating dinner
2. studying all night
3. Waiting for the bus
4. Meeting new people
5. Winning the writing contest
6. Painting landscapes
7. Attending red carpet events
8. Walking in the heavy rain
9. Drinking a cup of hot chocolate
10. making new friends

B. 1. Screaming wildly, the (child) threw a tantrum in the store.
2. The (ballerinas) dancing in the front row are supposed to be the best.
3. Terrified of falling off, (Devin) hung on tightly to the horse's reins.
4. Exhausted after hours of practice, the (boys) suggested taking a rest.
5. Knowing it was wrong, (Lina) still cheated on the test.
6. My (muffins) baking in the oven will be very delicious.
7. Lost in the mall, (Jessica) finally asked for directions.

C. 1. N 2. N
3. ADV 4. ADJ
5. ADV 6. ADJ
7. ADV

D. (Individual writing)

E. (Individual phrases)

7 More on Phrases

A. 1. ✔
2. Circle: The man sitting on the bench
3. ✔
4. ✔
5. Circle: such a warm and welcoming reception
6. ✔
7. Circle: a delicious cheesecake
8. ✔
9. ✔
10. ✔
11. Circle: that thick, oily, green substance
12. ✔

B. (Individual phrases)

C. 1. The coach of the opposing team did not think it was fair. ; Adj
2. That afternoon, all the workers assembled in the compound. ; Adv
3. The fugitive crawled through the tunnel and escaped. ; Adv
4. The members of the team were each given a name tag. ; Adj
5. No one from his group wanted to do the presentation. ; Adj
6. Fred played video games from morning to night. ; Adv
7. All the guests waited in the hallway. ; Adv
8. His little dog managed to jump across the ditch. ; Adv
9. The food in the cooler had gone bad. ; Adj
10. He climbed up the tall tree to save the cat. ; Adv
11. The guards of the palace ordered us to leave. ; Adj
12. The red jelly beans were scattered all over the place. ; Adv

D. 1. about superheroes
2. with a strawberry on it
3. of our school
4. before lunch
5. quite surprisingly
6. very happily

8 Active and Passive Voice

A. 1. A 2. A 3. P 4. A
5. P 6. P 7. A 8. P
9. A 10. A

B. 1. Mrs. Kelcher was directing (a musical production).
2. (The musical production) was introduced by Principal Santos.
3. (The musical) would be attended by the entire school.
4. Richard and Ivy created (the costumes).
5. (The props) were made by the art students.
6. Andre wrote (the songs for the school musical).
7. The students rehearsed (the musical) one last time before the performance.
8. Many teachers, students, and their parents attended (the show).
9. The actors read (their lines) backstage.
10. Sharon conducted (the band).
11. (The music) was played by the school band.
12. The audience cheered at the end of band's performance.
13. (Every actor) was congratulated by Mrs. Kelcher and Principal Santos.

C. 1. The Shelby Food for Kids Foundation was created by Grace Shelby.
2. A rare dinosaur fossil was discovered by Dr. Godfried.
3. The match of the century was watched by 2.3 million viewers.
4. All the dishes for the meal were cooked by my sister.
5. The notice on the board was posted by Jeremy.
6. All of my friends received the spam e-mail.
7. Eunice returned the overdue library book at last.
8. An anonymous person delivered the package.

9. Chef Aguilar created the special menu.
10. Dad assembled all the cabinets.

D. 1. ✘
2. ✔
3. ✔
4. ✔

Rewritten Sentences in the Passive Voice:
2. My neighbour's car was stolen last night.
3. The riddle cannot be solved within a minute.
4. The criminal was sentenced to two years in jail.

9 Direct and Indirect Speech

A. 1. D
2. D
3. D
4. I
5. I
6. D
7. I
8. D
9. I
10. I

B. 1. Clarissa said that nobody had told her about the surprise party.
2. John explained that the party had been very spontaneous.
3. Melody said that that movie made her cry.
4. The woman replies that she does not need that.
5. My little brother yells that he does not know where it is.
6. The children said that they were having a great time.

C. 1. Alex told his dad that he had not played in the game the day before.
2. Ron said that it had happened a week before.
3. The waiter said that they were serving fresh seafood that day.
4. Brandon told Ginny that she had to tell him the next day.
5. Molly said that Grandma would come two days later.
6. Stan told Mr. Will that his dog had eaten his homework the previous night.
7. The teacher told the class that they would have an outing the following week.
8. Bill said that they had gone to Hamilton the week before.

D. 1. Mrs. Watson asked Ben which was the one he wanted.
2. The police officer asked if I had come from that way.
3. The lady asked the cashier how much she owed.
4. Angela asked the boy what his name was.
5. Mrs. Healey asked the children if they had seen her cat.

10 The Mood of Sentences

A. Indicative Mood: 2, 4, 8
Imperative Mood: 1, 3, 6, 9
Subjunctive Mood: 5, 7

B. 1. were
2. were
3. book
4. were ; would
5. pay
6. were
7. move

C. (Suggested writing)
1. When his mom demanded to know who broke the vase, Damon pretended as if he were clueless.
2. Valerie's mom suggested that Valerie leave her project until the next day.
3. The teacher demanded that Jeremy apologize to Patricia for his rudeness.
4. If Debbie were taller, she would be able to ride on the roller coaster.
5. The doctor suggests that Mr. Sherwood get up earlier and exercise for half an hour before going to work.

D. (Individual writing)

11 Clauses

A. 1. I
2. D
3. I
4. D
5. I
6. I
7. D
8. I
9. D
10. I
11. I

B. 1. (D) Wherever she goes, | (I) she carries her doll with her.
2. (D) As I was going home, | (I) I saw Beth's little cousin.
3. (D) If she had asked more politely, | (I) I would have agreed to help.
4. (I) They gave up | (D) because there was too little time.
5. (D) However hard they tried, | (I) they could not make it.
6. (I) I would definitely go with you | (D) if I knew he was there.
7. (D) Because the weather was so bad, | (I) we cancelled the trip.
8. (D) If you want to succeed, | (I) you must put in effort and persevere.
9. (I) She walks her dog | (D) when she has nothing better to do.

C. (Individual writing)

D. It was Lucy's mom's birthday and Lucy wanted to buy her the perfect gift. Lucy was running out of time though (since the surprise party was only a couple of days away). She thought about buying her mom a necklace but she already had many necklaces. She thought about buying her a dress but her mom already had too many. Lucy sat on her bed thinking about what her mom needed (that she did not already have). After much thought, Lucy finally had an idea. Her worries were all gone (when she remembered what her mom always told her). (Whenever Lucy found it hard to get a gift for a friend), her mom would say, "The best gift comes from the heart." (So although Lucy was not a great painter), she made a painting of herself and her mom together. It was her mom's favourite gift ever.

12 Sentences

A. 1. or
2. and
3. and
4. but
5. but
6. and
7. or
8. but
9. or

B. 1. ✔ ; Since it was Alex's birthday
2. ✔ ; While I was waiting
3. ✔ ; Although she did not tell me
4. ✘
5. ✘
6. ✔ ; even though he has failed three times already
7. ✔ ; since the scenery there was breathtaking
8. ✘
9. ✔ ; If Annie's grandparents come to visit this summer

C. 1. When he heard the news, he was thrilled and he ran upstairs to tell his father.
2. If it rains, we will not go to the park but we can watch a video at Jason's place.
3. Rosa is such a kind person and she always makes friends wherever she goes.
4. While I painted the room, Lily carried boxes from the car and Kate arranged the furniture.

D. (Individual writing)

13 Punctuation

A. 1. The storm left the village with flooded basements, fallen trees, and mudslides.
2. Our nanny, Stefanie, got a new job.
3. Although I did not see it happen, I could feel the horror.
4. The incident happened on June 19, 2004.
5. Vera put on her shiny, diamond tiara for the ball last night.
6. The little boy replied, "I just asked for some candies."
7. Consequently, the student will have to redo the test.
8. Did you see the sleek, blue sports car on the highway?
9. Once we start, we should continue and not give up.

B. 1.
2.
3. ✔ ; Our dog, which everyone loves, likes eating treats.
4.
5. ✔ ; She let me see her camera, which was as thin as a credit card.
6.
7.
8.
9. ✔ ; Pam's younger sister, who looks very much like her, will come to the party too.
10.
11. ✔ ; Mrs. Steele, whose son is about my age, bakes great cookies.

C. (Write the colons in red.)
1. ✔
2. The article "Travel in Asia: China and India" is an interesting read.
3. We expect only one thing from him: complete the project by next Monday.
4. Do remember this: never ever give up.
5. We all have the same goal: win the tournament this time.
6. ✔
7. ✔

D. 1. He was introduced to the following people: Jason, Peter's cousin; Mandy, his boss's daughter; Sam, the secretary's husband.
2. It was chilly out there; the temperature dropped to a mere 2°C.
3. They met with John; it was a brief meeting.
4. No one wanted to leave; they were all eager for the announcement.
5. She is such a popular athlete; wherever she goes, she is surrounded by fans.

(Individual sentence)

14 More on Punctuation

A. 1. The final showdown – the do-or-die game – will be telecast live.
2. Everything boiled down to one word – perseverance.
3. *The Greatest Game Ever Played* – the story of an underdog golfer – is the best motivational film I have ever watched.
4. Apples, pears, and melons – these are the fruits we need for the salad.
5. I should tell her the truth – I was the one who accidentally lost her necklace.
6. The one rule they had – to not speak loudly – was not followed.
7. No matter what you do – explain, plead, or beg – it will not change her mind.

B. 1. The new manager is a twenty-three-year-old graduate.
2. This is a once-in-a-lifetime chance that you should not miss.
3. He lives in a twenty-six-year-old split-level bungalow.
4. Jordan's mother-in-law came to visit them for two weeks.
5. The school exams will be from mid-November to mid-December.
6. Many people were inspired by his from-rags-to-riches story.
7. Elisa's research shows that two-thirds of the population is under fifty-five years of age.

C. 1. The supporting role **(**Captain Truman**)** was given to a little-known actor by the name of Willie Whitt.
2. ✔
3. The honour students **(**of which I am one**)** are invited to the ceremony.
4. ✔
5. The students should **(**a**)** get a form, **(**b**)** fill it out, **(**c**)** get their parents' consent, and **(**d**)** return it to their teacher before noon tomorrow.
6. The graph **(**Fig. 2b**)** shows the population growth over the past 20 years.
7. ✔
8. The merger **(**yet to be confirmed**)** is set to take effect in January next year.

D. 1. Roberta Bondar became the first female astronaut to go into space. She received the Order of Canada**...**Roberta was named to the Canadian Medical Hall of Fame in 1998.
2. There are many ways to conserve energy**...** more and more people switch to driving small cars which are more fuel efficient.
3. Smart phones are becoming so dangerous for people, for example, some people forget to look both ways before crossing a street**...**that some organizations are promoting safe smart phone use and habits.
4. Recent research indicates that most of the asteroids orbit the sun**...**the chance of an asteroid striking the Earth is one in a million.

Review 2

A. 1. Duff hungrily gobbled everything.
2. an indefinite pronoun
3. I taught chemistry for many years.
4. future progressive tense
5. a participle
6. noun
7. an infinitive phrase
8. The boy in the blue shirt cried.
9. The book was written by Anne.
10. one tense back
11. Ron says that he will swim the next day.
12. subjunctive
13. make a command
14. can stand on its own
15. **,**
16. a conjunction
17. two independent clauses and one dependent clause
18. a colon
19. enclose additional information
20. a hyphen

B. Noun: 1, 15
Verb: 4, 12
Adjective: 5, 8, 11
Adverb: 10, 16
Pronoun: 6, 17
Preposition: 2, 3, 14
Conjunction: 9, 13
Interjection: 7, 18

As part of her summer ❶ vacation, Rachel travelled ❷ from Ottawa, Canada to Cushendall, Ireland. (She)[blue] stayed with her Aunt Anne and Uncle Pat ❸ for three weeks. (They)[blue] ❹ lived in a large house in the ❺ rolling countryside. ❻ (It)[blue] was her first time in Ireland and (she)[blue] did not know (what)[green] to expect.

When Rachel arrived, (she)[blue] exclaimed, "❼ Wow! This place is beautiful!" (It)[blue] was a warm and ❽ sunny day. Rachel was eager to play outside ❾ but (she)[blue] had to unpack her things ❿ neatly first. As (she)[blue] was unpacking, (she)[blue] was introduced to (someone)[red] (whom)[green] (she)[blue] had never met before. (It)[blue] was Murphy, her aunt and uncle's Golden Retriever. (He)[blue] was very ⓫ friendly with (them)[blue] and soon ⓬ started following Rachel around. ⓭ After Rachel had finished unpacking, (she)[blue] went outside to play ⓮ in the grass with Murphy.

Murphy discovered an old tree ⓯ stump and kept sniffing ⓰ curiously behind ⓱ (it)[blue]. Rachel went over to see (what)[green] (he)[blue] had found. ⓲ Oh! (It)[blue] was (something)[red] beyond her wildest imagination!

C. Simple Present: 3
Simple Past: 1, 7
Simple Future: 4
Present Progressive: 6
Past Progressive: 2, 8
Future Progressive: 5

D. A: gerund
B: participle
C: infinitive
1. C
2. A
3. B

E. NP:
A delicious, mouth-watering dinner ; her second wish ; a shiny red bike
Adj. P:
worried looking ; excited, high-pitched ; on its handlebar
Adv. P:
quite soundly ; on the pillow ; out of thin air

F. 1. P
2. A
3. A
4. A
5. P

G. A ; A ; C ; B

H. Rachel was desperate to find her new bike – she had never been this attached to anything before. She considered the following options: **(1)** look for the thief herself, **(2)** post flyers everywhere, and **(3)** use her third wish to find her bike.

compound
Rachel weighed her options and she picked the third one. She said to the leprechaun, "For my third wish, I want to know who took my bike."

compound-complex
After he made sure Rachel's third wish was well thought out, the leprechaun smiled and he told her to look around the corner.
When she peeked around the corner, Rachel saw a boy with her bike! He explained that he lost his bike the day before and he found it just then. The leprechaun attempted to explain, "I did warn you to think carefully..."

complex
Before he could say anything else, Rachel hugged him. She was happy because nothing could be better than meeting a wish-granting leprechaun in the first place!

Answers

Section 3

1 Computer Words

A. 1. online
2. mainframe
3. operation
4. download
5. machine
6. memory
7. mathematical
8. computer

B. 1. app
2. browser
3. pasted
4. firewall ; virus
5. gigabytes
6. blog
7. junk mail
8. password
9. uploaded
10. USB flash drive

C. A: CPU
B: web camera
C: monitor
D: speaker
E: keyboard
F: mouse
(Individual writing)

2 Measurement Words

A. B ; H ; E ; G ; F ; D ; I ; C ; A

B. (Suggested answers)
inch: a unit of measure equal to one twelfth of a foot
metric: a system of measurement based on the metre as a unit of length
distance: the length of space between two things
standard: used or accepted as the norm

C. 1. M 2. NM 3. NM 4. NM
5. M 6. M 7. NM 8. NM
9. NM 10. M 11. NM 12. M
13. NM 14. M

D. 1. kilometres
2. feet
3. acres
4. tablespoons
5. degrees Celsius
6. minutes
7. seconds
8. hours
9. centimetres

E. cup ; tablespoons ; teaspoon ; millilitres ; grams
3. minute ; seconds

3 Physical Activity Words

A.

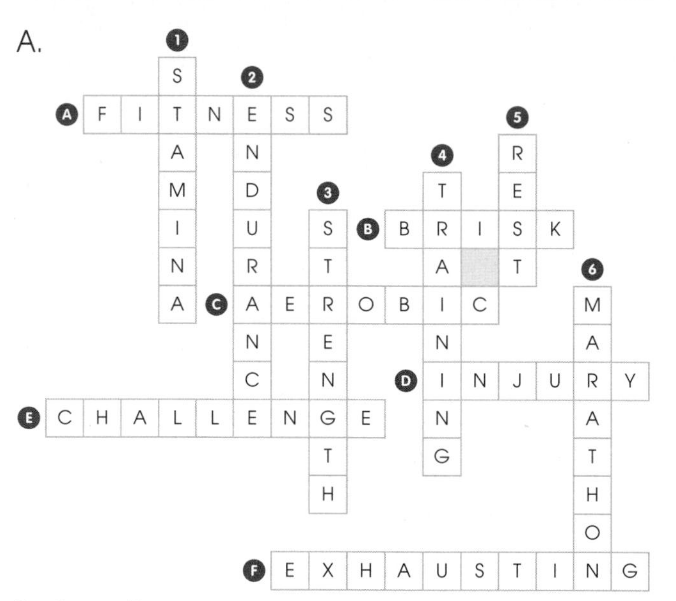

B. 1. active
2. Kinesiology
3. judo
4. motivation
5. muscles
6. physician
7. nutrients
8. recovers
9. warm up
10. routine
11. healthful
12. stretching

C. 1. push up
 2. skipping
 3. squat
 4. sit up
 5. plank
 6. handstand

4 Fantasy Words

A. 1. dragon
 2. hobbit
 3. fictional
 4. fantasy
 5. monster
 6. wizard
 7. creature
 8. heroic
 9. goblin
 10. novel

B. 1. fairy
 2. centaur
 3. phoenix
 4. a. unicorn b. mermaid
 5. a. troll b. elf
 6. dwarf
 7. werewolf
 8. vampire

C.

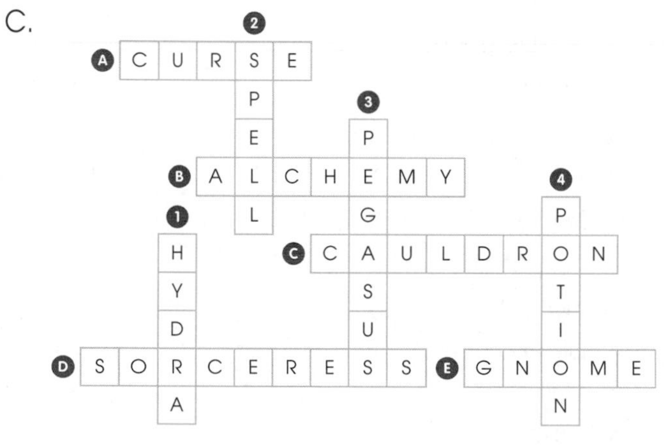

5 Hockey Words

A. 1. hockey
 2. NHL
 3. record
 4. season
 5. MVP
 6. offence
 7. WHA
 8. Stanley Cup
 9. pinpoint passing
 10. trade
 11. assist
 (Suggested answers)
 12. an enclosed area with seating used for sports and entertainment
 13. a set space that a ball or puck must enter in order for a team to score a point
 14. a group of sports teams that compete against one another for a championship
 15. the number of points made or lost in a game

B. 1. bar down
 2. rebounded
 3. Elbowing
 4. dekes
 5. rink
 6. faceoff
 7. blueliner
 8. zones
 9. referee
 10. hat-trick
 11. muffin
 12. biscuit
 13. netminder

C. 1. helmet
 2. shoulder pad
 3. glove
 4. stick
 5. hockey sock
 6. elbow pad
 7. hockey pants
 8. skate

6 Book Words

A. 1. font
2. publish
3. ligature
4. information
5. flourish
6. scribe
7. folio
8. text
9. literature
10. printing press
11. handwritten
12. script
13. Gothic

B. 1. author
2. epilogue
3. autobiography
4. library
5. journal
6. bookshop
7. Science fiction
8. publishers
9. Calligraphy
10. synopsis
11. table of contents

C. 1. pages
2. spine
3. title
4. illustration
5. publisher's logo
6. author
7. synopsis
8. quote
9. barcode

7 Geography Words

A. A: continental plate
B: continental drift
C: Panthalassa
D: meteorologist
E: magma
F: Pangaea
G: continent
H: topography
I: Earth
J: geophysicist
K: Rodinia
L: land mass
Supercontinent: F, K
Global Ocean: C
Geography Professional: D, J

B. A: North America
B: South America
C: Europe
D: Asia
E: Africa
F: Australia

C. 1. compass rose
2. equator
3. Global Positioning System
4. landforms
5. border
6. Cartography
7. archipelago
8. meridian ; North
9. Arctic

D. 1. butte
2. mountain range
3. island
4. plain
5. canyon
6. valley
7. plateau

8 Dessert Words

A. 1. Dessert
2. syrup
3. honey
4. cake
5. custard
6. pastry
7. chocolate
8. Pudding
9. mousse
10. powdered sugar

B. 1. semifreddo
2. malva pudding
3. gulab jamun
4. baklava
5. cremeschnitte

(Individual drawing and writing)

C.

More Dessert Words

cream puff
meringue
ice cream sandwich
cheesecake
waffle
soufflé
sundae

9 Baseball Words

A. 1. sports
2. contract
3. MVP
4. major league
5. championship
6. batting
7. varsity
8. rookie
9. season
10. home base
11. World Series
12. home run

B. 1. inning
2. on-deck
3. bench
4. goose egg
5. money pitch
6. curveball
7. aboard
8. cheese
9. hammer
10. southpaw
11. power hitter

C.

Centre Field
Left Field
Right Field
Short Stop
Second Base
First Base
Third Base
Pitcher
Catcher

10 Constellation Words

A. 1. the sun
 2. Ursa Major
 3. the Big Dipper
 4. Ursa Minor
 5. navigate
 6. the North Star
 7. Orion
 8. stars
 9. Lyra
 10. celestial equator
 11. zodiac signs
 12. Cassiopeia
 13. constellation
 14. celestial

B. (Individual drawing)

C. April: Aries
 May: Taurus
 June: Gemini
 July: Cancer
 August: Leo
 September: Virgo
 October: Libra
 November: Scorpio
 December: Sagittarius
 January: Capricorn
 February: Aquarius
 March: Pisces

11 Charity Words

A. E ; D ; A ; F ; B ; C

B. Raise ; hope ; Volunteer ; donation ; Contribute ; walkathon ; give ; Support

C. 1. aid
 2. benevolent
 3. relief
 4. needy
 5. endow
 6. humane
 7. welfare
 8. cause

D. 1. cause
 2. benevolent
 3. welfare
 4. humane

E. (Individual writing)

12 Sustainability Words

A. 1. F
 2. B
 3. E
 4. J
 5. A
 6. G
 7. K
 8. C
 9. D
 10. L
 11. H
 12. I

B. 1. renewable
 2. Wind
 3. Donating
 4. footprint
 5. ease
 6. ecohouse
 7. biodegradable
 8. reuse
 9. commitment

C. 1. LED bulbs
 2. compost
 3. conserve water
 4. energy-efficient appliances
 5. donate clothes

13 Carnival Words

A. 1. spectators
2. carnival
3. carousel
4. juggler
5. tightrope walking
6. trapeze
7. cotton candy ; ticket

B.

entertainer: ringmaster, acrobat, juggler, magician, clown

entertainment: bumper cars, carousel, tightrope walking, Ferris wheel, trapeze, fireworks

C.

Carnival Word	Definition
1. stilt walking	using a pair of long poles with footrests to walk
2. contortionist	a person who can bend his or her body into unnatural positions
3. puppet show	a theatrical performance using inanimate objects controlled by wires
4. unicycle	a vehicle that looks like a bicycle but has only one wheel
5. parade	a march including bands and floats

6. puppet show
7. stilt walking
8. unicycle
9. contortionist
10. parade

D.

Across: ACROBAT, COTTON CANDY, CLOWN, JUGGLER

Down: PARADE, CARNIVAL, TICKET, CAROUSEL, UNICYCLE

14 Accessory Words

A. 1. belt ; C
2. wallet ; D
3. sunglasses ; E
4. flats ; A
5. brooch ; B

B. 1. bangle
2. earrings
3. headgear
4. sneakers
5. sandals

C. 1. boots
2. Mittens
3. earmuffs
4. shawls
5. toque
6. glove
7. scarf

D. Headgear: cap, beanie, beret, chupalla
Footwear: sandals, slippers, flip flops, high heels
(Individual examples and drawings)

Review 3

A. 1. memory
2. furlong
3. non-metric
4. endurance
5. a fairy
6. hobbit
7. a deke
8. a ligature
9. font
10. Rodinia
11. malva pudding
12. Most Valuable Player
13. Lyra
14. Polaris
15. Volunteer
16. using the dishwasher
17. avoid wasteful use of
18. a Ferris wheel
19. hats
20. flip-flops

B. 1. active ; routine ; stretching ; muscles
2. curveball ; fastball
3. third base ; inning
4. arena ; offence ; record ; goal

t	a	c	u	r	v	e	b	a	l	l	u	t	i	n	e	a
h	r	e	c	o	r	d	r	o	f	a	s	t	b	a	l	l
i	a	c	t	u	t	h	i	r	d	b	a	s	e	r	a	a
s	t	r	e	t	c	h	i	n	g	c	u	r	v	e	r	c
d	c	t	i	i	g	o	a	m	o	f	f	e	n	c	e	t
i	n	i	i	n	n	i	n	g	a	c	t	i	v	o	n	i
a	c	t	i	e	v	e	m	u	l	s	c	l	e	g	a	v
b	a	a	q	t	i	v	e	m	u	s	c	l	e	s	o	e

C. 1. online
2. mouse
3. downloaded
4. monitor
5. literature
6. illustrations
7. mythical creatures
8. author
9. synopsis
10. heroic
11. Monster
12. wizard
13. dragon

D.

Dawson's Desserts Charity Fundraiser

July 18
Sunday

Our signature desserts include:

soft and fluffy — soufflé
sweet and syrupy — gulab jamun
light and creamy — cremeschnitte
cool and smooth — semifreddo

Support Dawson's Desserts in its annual charity dessert fundraiser. All proceeds will be donated to improve the welfare of those in need. Contribute to a good cause and buy some of our delicious desserts!

E. (Suggested answers)
1. The acrobat and the contortionist accomplished amazing feats.
2. We ate cotton candy as we watched the fireworks.
3. The bumper cars were almost as fun as the Ferris wheel.
4. The magician brought a spectator on stage for his final act.
5. A clown was juggling as another clown was stilt walking.

F.
1. landform
2. archipelago
3. continental drift
4. Panthalassa
5. Pangaea
6. topography

- one big global ocean that surrounded Pangaea
- the way a region looks on the surface of the Earth
- the supercontinent that existed millions of years ago
- hills, valleys, canyons, plains, and basins are examples of this
- a group of islands on a stretch of water
- slow movement of the continental plates on the Earth's surface

G. 1. Orion
2. Ursa Minor
3. Cassiopeia

1 The Gordian Knot

A. 1. in Turkey
2. Telmissus
3. a Phrygian god
4. two

B. 1. The metaphor is the phrase "Gordian knot", which refers to an intractable problem solved by a bold solution.
2. The Phrygians instantly proclaim him king and rename the kingdom Gordium in his honour.
3. The oracle's second prophecy is that whosoever unravels the intricate knot will rule all of Asia.
4. He "unravels" the Gordian Knot by cutting it in half with his sword.

C. 1. Protagonist: King Arthur
Antagonist: Mordred
2. As the king, Arthur's main plight is fighting the Saxons who are invading his lands.
3. (Suggested answer)
The magical elements include the wizard Merlin, who places a sword in a stone using magic so as to prove the identity of the true king, as well as Arthur receiving the sword Excalibur from a sorceress. Also, at the end, Arthur is taken to the mystical island of Avalon.
4. (Individual answer)

D. (Individual writing)

2 Dandelion

A. 1. a poem
2. six
3. stained
4. dandelions

B. 1. This poem is a narrative poem because it tells a story.
2. The speaker's neighbours do not like the dandelions because they miss the green grass.
3. Yes, the dandelions return in spring the following year.
4. In the last stanza, the narrator describes the dandelions as not dandy because no one is happy about them being there.

C. 1. The acrostic poem is about dandelions blowing in the wind and landing on the ground.
2. (Individual writing)
3. (Individual writing)

D. (Individual writing)

3 The Bully

A. 1. in the back
2. egg salad sandwich
3. jealous
4. happy

B. 1. (Suggested answer)
The theme of this short story is about sympathizing with others and understanding where they are coming from and being kind to those in need.
2. The characters in this short story are Mia, her mom, and the bully.
3. The bully is jealous of Mia because she has lunch while the bully does not.
4. Mia's solution is to help the bully by bringing her a sandwich for lunch so that she will not be hungry.

C. (Individual writing and drawings)

D. (Individual writing)

4 The Beauties and the Boastful King

A. 1. Fanta
2. Alfonso
3. a hooded figure
4. throws witch's fire

B. 1. The fantasy element of this story is that it is set in an imaginary world with imaginary characters, and involves supernatural elements such as witch's fire.
2. King Humza is insulted by King Alfonso's pretentious claim because he thinks only a goddess may have a day of celebration dedicated to her.
3. Witch's fire is magical fire that is brighter than the sun and burns hotter than any flame on earth.
4. At the end of the story, King Alfonso learns that a person's heart matters more than his or her look.

C. (Individual writing)

D. (Individual writing)

5 Andromeda and Perseus

A. 1. in Aethiopia
2. foolish pride
3. Cetus
4. in the northern sky

B. 1. The moral lesson of this myth is to not have foolish pride.
2. They sacrifice Andromeda to the sea monster by chaining her to a sea cliff.
3. Perseus wants to save Andromeda because he has fallen in love with her.
4. Yes, Cassiopeia is punished for her vanity by Poseidon, who places her in the heavens, chained to a throne to revolve upside down for eternity.

C. (Individual answers)

D. (Individual writing)

6 Super Boys

A. 1. Super Boys
2. a beauty contest
3. They mismatch the garbage lids.
4. originality and creativity

B. 1. It has six panels.
2. It tells the reader that the town is holding a neighbourhood beauty contest and that the Super Boys think they can help their neighbourhood win the contest.
3. The purpose of the speech bubbles is to show what the characters are saying.
4. The Super Boys help their neighbourhood win the beauty contest by cleaning the neighbourhood and covering all the garbage bins with lids.

C. (Individual writing and sketching)

D. (Individual drawing and writing)

7 The Purrrfect Fundraiser

A. 1. Purrrfect Pets Animal Shelter
2. at a community park
3. six hours
4. the advertising team

B. 1. The purpose of this ad is to promote the fundraiser so people will come to it.
2. At the fundraiser, people can get their faces painted and learn how to create a 3-D model of their favourite animal.
3. Proceeds will go toward saving and caring for the homeless and sick animals that Purrrfect Pets Animal Shelter has rescued over the years.
4. The vets and staff help nurse the animals back to health. This includes providing them with the medication, love, and care that they desperately need.

C. 1. The purpose of this ad is to persuade people to visit The Shadow House.
2. The slogan is "The scariest house in the world!"
3. The font size grabs the reader's attention and the style complements the creepiness of the haunted mansion. This makes the ad more effective.

D. (Individual writing)

E. (Individual design)

8 Rainforest Animals

A. 1. the poison dart frog
2. the jaguar
3. the piranha
4. the spider monkey

B. 1. Heading: Rainforest Animals
Subheadings:
Spider Monkey ; Poison Dart Frog ; Jaguar ; Piranha ; Toucan ; Anaconda
2. It got its name from its long spider-like limbs and tail.
3. The poison dart frog's diet is composed of insects, like termites, flies, and ants.
4. The anaconda catches its food by waiting underwater to catch its prey.

C. (Individual colouring)
1. The heading is "Renewable Energy Sources".
2. The subheadings are "Wind Power", "Solar Power", "Hydroelectric Power", and "Biomass Power".
3. (Suggested answer)
The use of colour makes it easier to understand this chart because it shows the reader visually which pictures go with what subheadings, thus making it easier to differentiate between them.
4. The layout and illustrations are important because they help the reader understand and visualize the different renewable energy sources, and thus make the text more effective.

D. (Individual diagram)

9 Pocahontas

A. 1. the Powhatan
2. playful one
3. Rebecca
4. an English settler

B. 1. The purpose of this biography is to inform readers of the real story of Pocahontas, and her role in American history.
2. Pocahontas helped the English by acting as an ally in negotiations with her father, as well as helping them survive summer droughts and bad winters.
3. Pocahontas lived among the English as a teenager because she was kidnapped and her father failed to negotiate her release.
4. The English wanted to show Pocahontas to England because they needed more colonists and Pocahontas was seen as an advocate for the cause.

C. (Individual writing)

D. (Individual writing and drawing)

10 The Brothers Grimm

A. 1. the Brothers Grimm
2. in Hanau
3. lawyer
4. a dictionary

B. 1. (Suggested example)
What is an anthology?
2. The Brothers Grimm came up with *Kinder-und Hausmärchen* after researching and collecting local folk tales and putting them together.
3. As adults, the brothers had financial difficulties and had to rely on friends and colleagues for assistance.
4. Their German dictionary was never completed because the brothers died before they could finish it.

C. (Individual writing)

D. (Individual writing and drawing)

11 Guinness World Records

A. 1. Sir Hugh Beaver
2. pub patrons
3. in 1955
4. in Australia

B. 1. The purpose of the caption is to give information about the image – the Burj Khalifa.
2. Sir Hugh Beaver thought a reference book was a good idea because it would offer definitive answers to arguments about trivial facts, as well as promote Guinness.
3. When the book was published in 1955, it became an instant bestseller and the No.1 selling book in Britain that year.
4. The bulldog ant is an achievement of nature.
5. The Burj Khalifa makes the record for the tallest building since 2008.

C. 1. heading
2. entry
3. explanation
4. diagram
5. caption
6. label
7. The diagram helps readers visualize the parts of a telescope to better understand how it works.
8. (Individual answer)
9. (Individual writing)

D. (Individual writing and drawing)

12 C. S. Lewis's Dedication to Education

A. 1. English and philosophy
2. a writers' group
3. the Inklings
4. educating

B. 1. The writer's opinion is that C. S. Lewis was not only a great writer but also a great educator.
2. Lewis voiced his religious beliefs by leading a club that debated religious issues, writing about spirituality, and broadcasting his views on his own radio program.
3. As a member of the Inklings, Lewis continued to learn by exchanging ideas with other writers.
4. C. S. Lewis was "more than an author" because he was also an educator. As a teacher, his success could not only be seen in how many books he sold but also in his students.

C. (Individual writing)

D. (Individual writing)

13 Kelly's Blog

A. 1. trying new things
2. at her friend's birthday party
3. anxious
4. every week

B. 1. The blog entry is about the importance of trying new things.
2. The blogger usually plays the same games after school, goes to the same mall on the weekends, and eats the same food every day.
3. It is important to try something new because otherwise life can get boring.
4. Some of the blogger's suggestions of new things to try include camping in your backyard, trying a food you have never tried before, or waking up an hour earlier than usual.

C. 1. Kelly's Corner
2. Today I Tried Something New
3. Kelly Kahn
4. January 5, 2019
5. (Check these features.)
menu/navigation bar ; blog posts ordered from last to first ; footer ; attention-grabbing title ; contact information ; tags ; comment section ; sidebar with social profile ; image(s) ; terms of use and copyright section

D. (Individual writing)
E. (Individual writing)

14 All about Good Food!

A. 1. heart disease
2. green and orange
3. protein
4. eating with your family

B. 1. (Individual answer)
2. It is easy and straightforward because it tells you about the different food groups that you should choose from on a daily basis and how much of them to eat.
3. Health Canada recommends we consume dark green and orange vegetables daily, as well as different grains, dairy products, and meats or alternatives.

C. 1. The company's name is Damien's Dangerously Delish Doughnuts.
2. They are advertising their selection of over 50 different flavours of doughnuts.
3. (Individual answer)

D. (Individual writing)
E. (Individual writing)

Review 4

A. 1. metaphor
2. real people, events, or places
3. a stanza
4. an acrostic poem
5. stanza
6. the antagonist
7. the supernatural
8. magical characters and creatures
9. a myth
10. gods and goddesses
11. a graphic novel
12. to persuade
13. a subheading
14. a heading, subheadings, and images
15. a biography
16. a textbook
17. to sell
18. a sidebar with a social profile
19. Call to Action
20. catchiness

B. 1. ✔
2.
3.
4. ✔
5. ✔
6. ✔
7.

C. 1. (Suggested answer)
Two features of a travel blog include a date and a photo. The date catalogues the precise time of the travel and the photo provides a visual aid to allow the reader to better imagine the place being described.
2. (Suggested answer)
The purpose is to be able to look back and better remember the trip, as well as catalogue details about all the places a person has visited.
3. The writer's favourite place in the palace is the Hall of Mirrors, which has 17 broad arcaded mirrors opposite 17 large windows overlooking the gardens, with beautiful glass chandeliers reflecting light off the mirrored surfaces.
4. The information given in the sidebar includes the writer's name, her brief biography, and her blog archive.

D. (Check these features.)
slogan ; persuasive language ; information about the product or service ; text in different fonts and sizes
(Individual writing)

E. (Individual writing)

1. (Suggested answers)
   HIND ; WIND ; WINE ; DINE ; PINE ; PANE ; PALE ; PALM
2. (Individual drawings)
   1. dolphin
   2. octopus
   3. fish
   4. sea turtle
   5. seahorse
   6. crab
   7. starfish
3.

w	t	y	u	q	v	o	b	u	i	b	m	s	g	d	k
g	s	a	n	e	o	g	g	o	l	f	e	c	s	w	o
h	t	v	c	f	l	c	y	s	b	u	t	b	m	p	u
o	e	m	s	g	l	t	m	r	a	g	t	s	e	g	s
a	g	o	s	t	e	n	n	i	s	a	g	o	c	b	p
k	d	l	u	e	y	k	a	l	k	a	y	c	i	a	f
l	e	p	r	c	b	e	s	t	e	a	s	c	b	m	o
t	b	y	f	g	a	h	t	m	t	o	s	e	r	o	c
e	h	b	i	e	l	o	i	s	b	s	k	r	a	l	b
p	y	a	n	g	l	c	c	s	a	h	i	c	s	m	o
p	u	s	g	o	c	k	s	a	l	r	i	g	i	a	k
a	k	c	b	a	s	e	b	a	l	l	n	c	s	n	g
o	j	o	d	k	a	y	a	k	i	n	g	g	t	o	l
d	p	t	a	s	w	i	m	m	i	n	g	p	j	b	h

4. (Suggested answers)
   1. doghouse
   2. bowtie
   3. yourself
   4. highway
   5. newspaper
   6. popcorn
   7. watershed
   8. earthquake
   9. supermarket
5. (Colour these pairs.)
   brief - leaf ; pearl - hurl ; flight - bite ; sour - flower ; salt - halt ; caught - bought ; steak - lake ; scale - whale
6. dish ; dash ; lash ; last ; lost ; lose ; love
7. sweet - sugary
   delicious - flavourful
   healthful - nutritious
   salty - savoury
   soft - hard
   cold - hot
   melted - frozen
   dry - moist
8. (Suggested answers)
   1. disappearance
   2. illogical
   3. prearrangement
   4. unreasonable
   5. ineffective
   6. subconsciously
   7. interactive
   8. imperfection
   9. interviewer
   10. unofficially
   11. unfriendly
   12. unequally
   13. disagreement
   14. indefinitely
9. 1. B 2. D 3. C 4. E
   5. A 6. I 7. F 8. H
   9. G
10. BE ; AGE ; TAPE ; GREAT ; REPEAT ; WEATHER ; PLEASANT ; STATEMENT ; ATTENDANCE
11. help ; held ; head ; heat ; meat ; meal
12. (Suggested words)
   1. love
   2. dessert
   4. understanding
   5. appreciation
   6. enthusiastically
13.

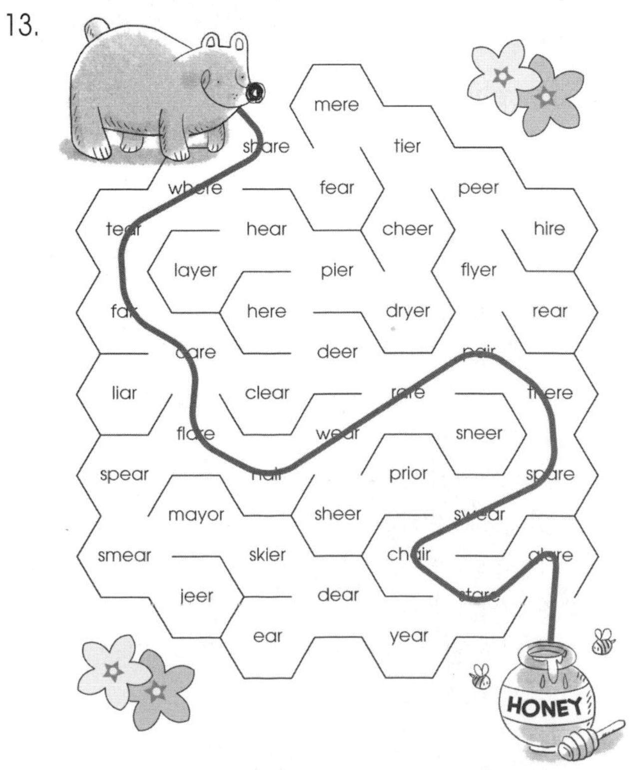

Language Games

Help Jack climb up the beanstalk by changing one letter at a time.

Vocabulary – Sea Animal Words

2 **Look at the outlines of the sea animals. Draw the details and write their names in the boxes.**

Circle the 12 sport words in the word search.

soccer **gymnastics** **skiing** **volleyball** **tennis** **swimming**

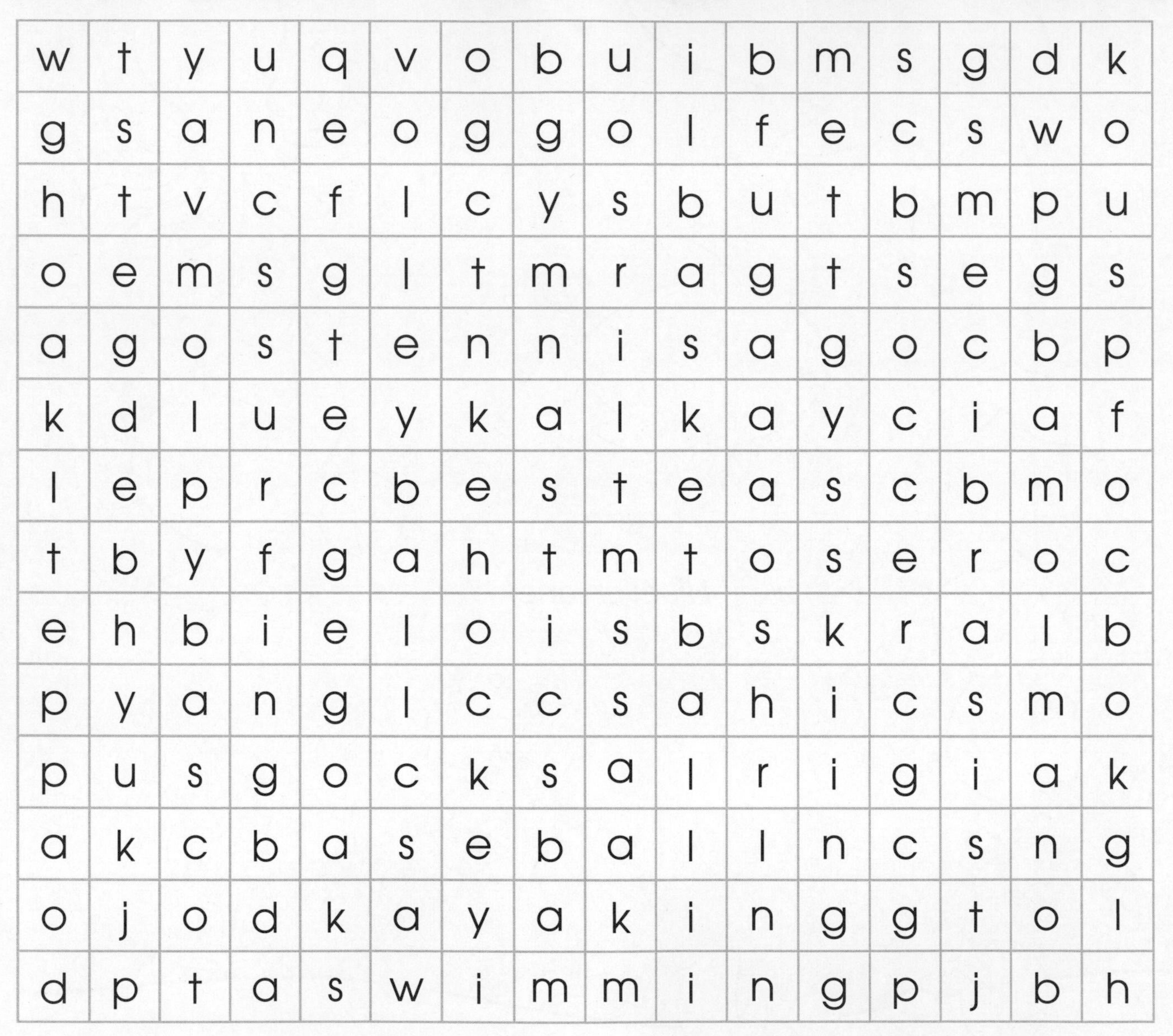

w	t	y	u	q	v	o	b	u	i	b	m	s	g	d	k
g	s	a	n	e	o	g	g	o	l	f	e	c	s	w	o
h	t	v	c	f	l	c	y	s	b	u	t	b	m	p	u
o	e	m	s	g	l	t	m	r	a	g	t	s	e	g	s
a	g	o	s	t	e	n	n	i	s	a	g	o	c	b	p
k	d	l	u	e	y	k	a	l	k	a	y	c	i	a	f
l	e	p	r	c	b	e	s	t	e	a	s	c	b	m	o
t	b	y	f	g	a	h	t	m	t	o	s	e	r	o	c
e	h	b	i	e	l	o	i	s	b	s	k	r	a	l	b
p	y	a	n	g	l	c	c	s	a	h	i	c	s	m	o
p	u	s	g	o	c	k	s	a	l	r	i	g	i	a	k
a	k	c	b	a	s	e	b	a	l	l	n	c	s	n	g
o	j	o	d	k	a	y	a	k	i	n	g	g	t	o	l
d	p	t	a	s	w	i	m	m	i	n	g	p	j	b	h

golf **kayaking** **hockey** **basketball** **surfing** **baseball**

4 Complete each compound word.

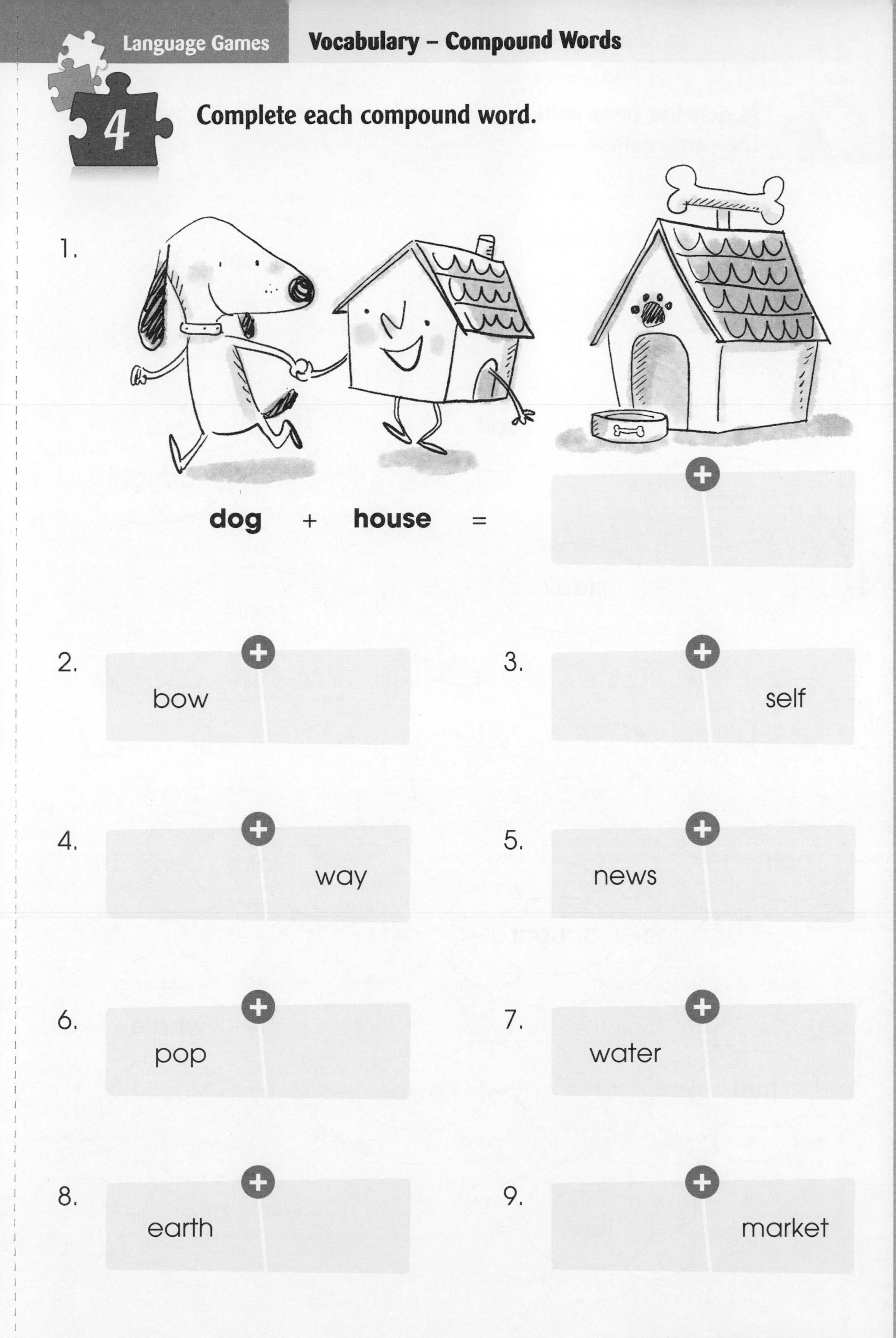

1. **dog** + **house** =

2. bow +

3. + self

4. + way

5. news +

6. pop +

7. water +

8. earth +

9. + market

Match the bees with the flowers by colouring each rhyming pair the same colour.

Change "fish" to "love" by changing one letter at a time.

fish

___ ___ ___ ___ ← You eat your food on a ______ .

___ ___ ___ ___ ← another word for "run"

___ ___ ___ ___ ← eye___ ___ ___ ___

___ ___ ___ ___ ← the opposite of "first"

___ ___ ___ ___ ← If you do not know where you are, you are ______ .

___ ___ ___ ___ ← My dad tends to ______ his car keys.

I ___ ___ ___ ___ you !

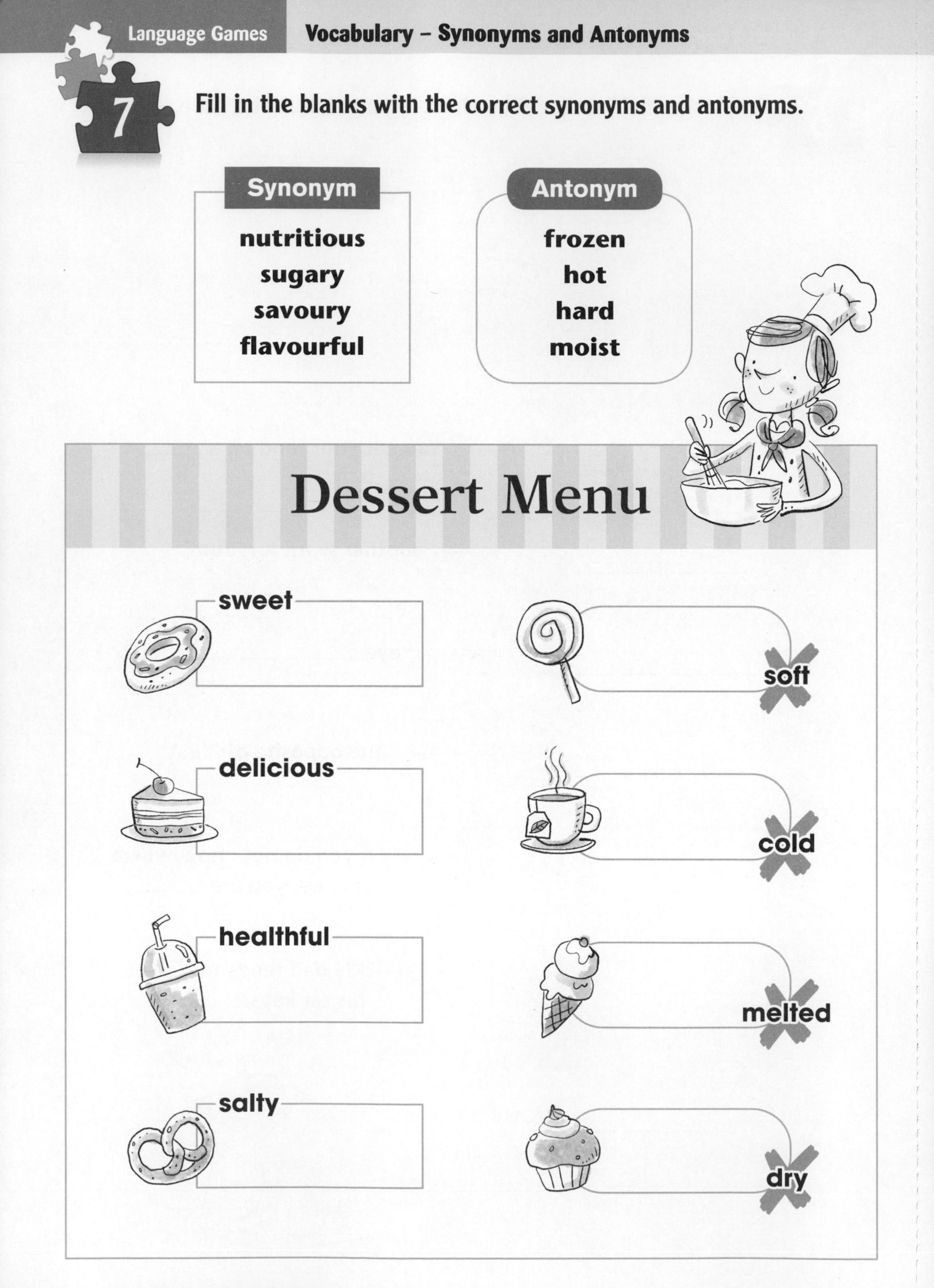
7
Fill in the blanks with the correct synonyms and antonyms.
Synonym
nutritious
sugary
savoury
flavourful
Antonym
frozen
hot
hard
moist
Dessert Menu
sweet
delicious
healthful
salty
soft
cold
melted
dry

11

Help Mimi the Mouse get the cheese by changing one letter at a time.

from ___ ___ ___ ___ to toe

the opposite of "cold"

the past tense of "hold"

Steak, lamb, beef, and bacon are different types of ___ ___ ___ ___ .

What do you say if you are in danger?

It is important to eat a balanced ___ ___ ___ ___ .

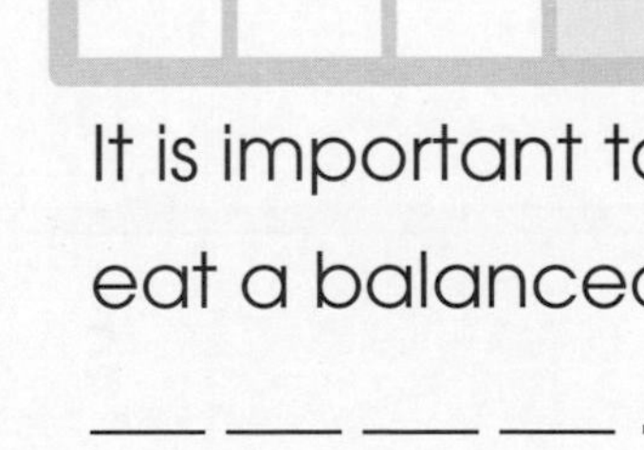

10

Complete the words using only the letters in the word "TEA" to bring Josie to her cat.

9

Look at the zoomed-in views of different means of transportation. Name them by writing the letters in the circles.

Transportation

- Ⓐ school bus
- Ⓑ airplane
- Ⓒ sailboat
- Ⓓ submarine
- Ⓔ bicycle
- Ⓕ hot-air balloon
- Ⓖ helicopter
- Ⓗ truck
- Ⓘ train

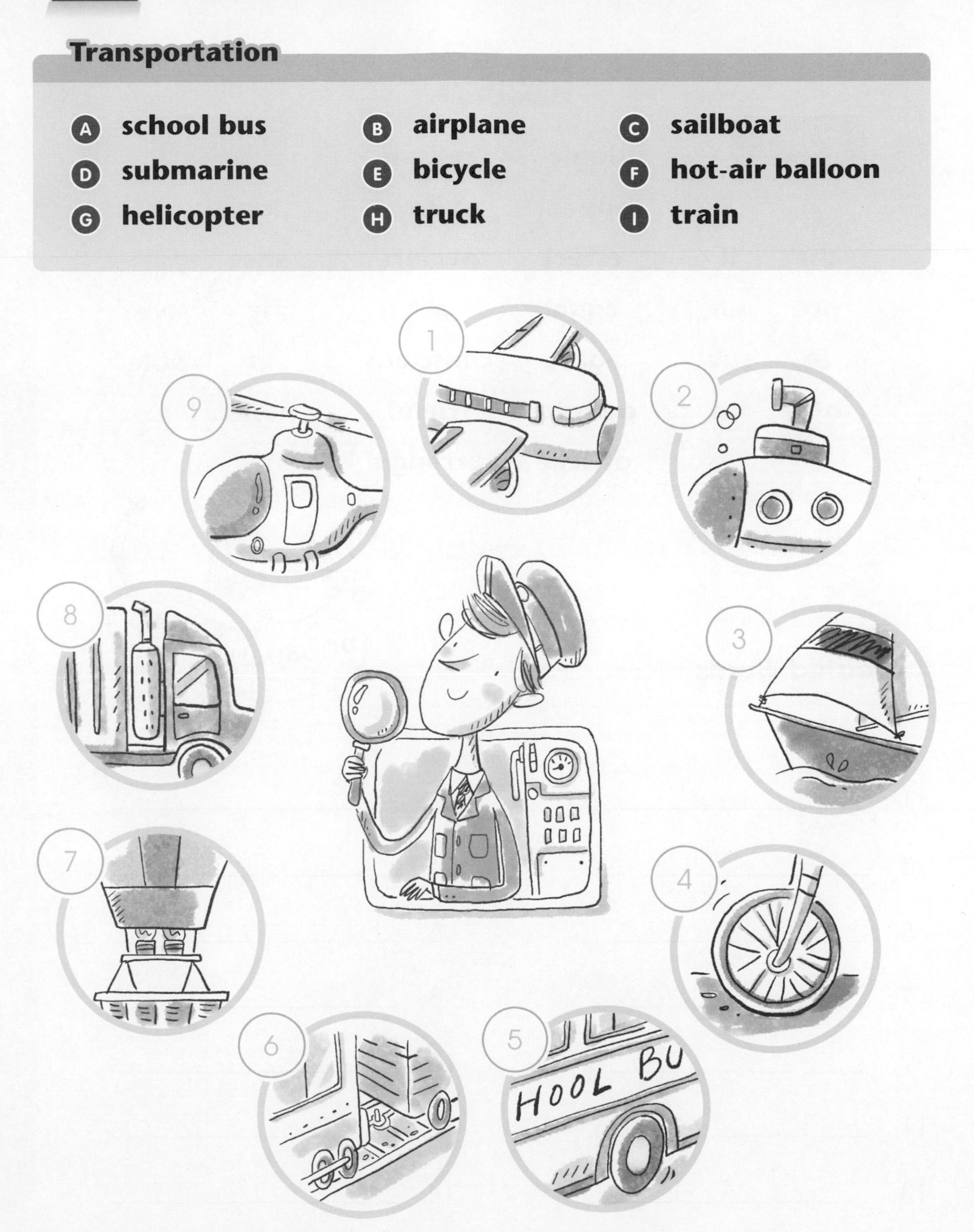

8

Create words by matching the word parts from the three groups.

Part 1

dis, il, pre, un, in, sub, inter, im

Part 2

logic, reason, appear, view, effect, perfect, equal, act, agree, conscious, definite, friend, official, arrange

Part 3

ion, ance, al, ly, ive, er, able, ment

Created Words

1. ____________________
3. ____________________
5. ____________________
7. ____________________
9. ____________________
11. ____________________
13. ____________________

2. ____________________
4. ____________________
6. ____________________
8. ____________________
10. ____________________
12. ____________________
14. ____________________

12

Write words with the given number of syllables.

Help Benny Bear find his pot of honey by following the words that rhyme with "bear".

We have an exciting Language Game Design Challenge! Submit your design to win a prize if your entry is selected and posted on our website!

Entry Rules:

- You have a passion for learning English.
- *Complete EnglishSmart* is your favourite learning tool.
- You are between 6 and 14 years old.

How to Enter:

1. Use the back of this page to create your own language game.
2. Give your language game a title.
3. Make sure the language game is fun!

My Contact Information

Name: ______________________ Age: ________

School: ______________________ Grade: ________

E-mail: ______________________

Parent's Signature

Scan and e-mail this form and your language game to: *ca-info@popularworld.com* or mail it to: 15 Wertheim Court, Units 602-603, Richmond Hill, Ontario, Canada L4B 3H7.

Popular Book Canada retains the right to use all the entries for promotional purposes. The chosen entries will be posted on our website and the winners will be contacted regarding the prize.